Publication Number 4

of the Mathematics Research Center
United States Army
The University of Wisconsin

FRONTIERS
OF NUMERICAL
MATHEMATICS

A symposium conducted by the
Mathematics Research Center,
United States Army and the
National Bureau of Standards
at the University of Wisconsin,
Madison, Wisconsin, October
30 and 31, 1959

edited by Rudolph E. Langer

Madison | The University of Wisconsin Press | 1960

Published by
THE UNIVERSITY OF WISCONSIN PRESS
430 Sterling Court, Madison 6, Wisconsin

Prepared for the camera by Phyllis J. Kern
Printed in the United States of America by the
George Banta Company, Inc. , Menasha, Wisconsin

Library of Congress Catalog Card Number 60-60026

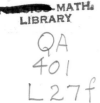
Participants

Lecturers

LEE ARNOLD
Chairman, Department of Aeronautics and Astronautics
New York University

GARRETT BIRKHOFF
Professor, Department of Mathematics
Harvard University

S. CHANDRASEKHAR
Distinguished Service Professor, Yerkes Observatory
University of Chicago

JOSEPH O. HIRSCHFELDER
Director, Theoretical Chemistry Laboratory
University of Wisconsin

ZDENĚK KOPAL
Member, Mathematics Research Center, and
Chairman, Department of Astronomy
University of Manchester

PHILIP M. MORSE
Director, Massachusetts Institute of Technology Computation Center,
Massachusetts Institute of Technology

WILLIAM PRAGER
L. Herbert Ballou University Professor
Brown University

J. SMAGORINSKY
Chief, General Circulation Research Section
U. S. Weather Bureau
Washington, D. C.

Invited Attendants

HANS F. BUECKNER
Member, Mathematics Research Center

F. A. FEND
General Electric Engineering Laboratories

H. L. GARABEDIAN
General Motors Research Laboratories

PETER HENRICI
Associate Professor, University of California

PHILIP G. HODGE, Jr.
Professor, Mechanics Department
Illinois Institute of Technology

A. S. HOUSEHOLDER
Chief, Mathematics Panel
Oak Ridge National Laboratory

DAVID R. HOWES
Engineering Command
Army Chemical Center

THOMAS F. KIMES
Mathematics Section, Westinghouse Electric Corporation

CORNELIUS LANCZOS
Member, Mathematics Research Center, and
Senior Professor, Institute for Advanced Studies
Dublin, Ireland

H. MELVIN LIEBERSTEIN
Member, Mathematics Research Center

O. L. MANGASARIAN
Applied Mathematics Department
Shell Development Company

W. R. MANN
Associate Professor, Department of Mathematics
University of North Carolina

PETER MUSEN
Assistant Professor, Astronomy Department
University of Cincinnati

GUY ORCUTT
Professor, Department of Economics,
University of Wisconsin

CODA H. T. PAN
Development Engineer
General Electric Company

J. B. ROSEN
Head, Applied Mathematics Department
Shell Development Company

DANIEL SHANKS
Consultant, Applied Mathematics Department
David Taylor Model Basin

DAVID YOUNG
Director, Computation Center
University of Texas

Foreword

This symposium, which was held at Madison, Wisconsin, on 30-31 October 1959, was conducted jointly by the Mathematics Research Center, United States Army, and the National Bureau of Standards. The meetings were held in the auditorium of the Wisconsin Center building on the campus of the University of Wisconsin. The symposium was opened by a message of welcome from the University's vice-president, Professor Fred H. Harrington.

There were eight lectures, each in a specific field, and each of about fifty minutes' length. Discussion periods were interspersed. The program committee consisted of:

> Dr. Franz L. Alt, National Bureau of Standards,
> Dr. Hans F. Bueckner, Mathematics Research Center,
> Dr. L. M. Milne-Thomson, Mathematics Research Center.

The purpose of the symposium should be clearly understood. It was not intended to be an occasion for the presentation of research results, but one for a survey of the future; for the identification of some mathematical problems that will have to be faced in the lines of scientific advance.

An informal social gathering in the Mathematics Research Center building was arranged by the ladies of the Center for early arrivals on the evening of 29 October. A general reception, in the lounge of the Wisconsin Center Building, was held in the evening of 30 October.

The meetings were presided over by the members of the program committee. The symposium was closed by cordial remarks from Dr. Alt on behalf of the National Bureau of Standards.

Preface

This twentieth century, unlike its predecessors, is one in which mathematicians, the world over, are essentially specialists. The explosive growth of mathematics has necessitated that. What concerns us here is the over-all dichotomy that has come to mark off the "pure" and the "applied".

Mathematicians with interests in the "pure" domain enshirine their subject for its own sake. They give reign to their imaginations to conceive new theories and amplify established ones, and pursue their developments objectively. They do not hesitate to mold and modify their problems to suit their tastes and capabilities. They refuse to moot the question of practical applicability of their results, disclaiming concern with it, or asserting, and indeed with much justice, that mathematical findings, however abstract or esoteric, do abundantly prove themselves, in the course of time, to be concretely applicable.

The "applied" mathematicians conceive their rôles differently. They face their problems and grapple with them as science or technology throws them up. Relevancy of their results to actuality is of the essence to them, and under this constraint they find but little latitude within which a problem can be tailored or simplified. They must generally meet complications head on. It is a satisfaction to them that the whole structure of science rests on the bed-rock they lay down.

This symposium was directed toward the applied mathematician. It was designed to scan the lines of expected scientific advance with an eye for the mathematical problems that loom there; for which, it seems, solutions will be needed. The speakers—path-finders and authorities in their various fields—were therefore asked to outline the impending mathematical tasks as they see them. It is hoped that these lectures will give mathematicians some measure of guidance for the orientation of their efforts.

Rudolph E. Langer

Contents

Page

Participants   v
Foreword   ix
Preface   x

Paper One, Stress Analysis in the Plastic Range   3
   WILLIAM PRAGER
   Discussion of Paper One   17

Paper Two, Some Mathematical Problems of Nuclear Reactor
   Theory   23
   GARRETT BIRKHOFF
   Discussion of Paper Two   43

Paper Three, Numerical Problems of Contemporary Celestial
   Mechanics   45
   ZDENĚK KOPAL
   Discussion of Paper Three   55

Paper Four, Aeroelasticity   59
   LEE ARNOLD
   Discussion of Paper Four   67

Paper Five, Operations Research   69
   PHILIP M. MORSE
   Discussion of Paper Five   79

Paper Six, Mathematical Bottlenecks in Theoretical Chemistry   83
   JOSEPH O. HIRSCHFELDER
   Discussion of Paper Six   97

Paper Seven, Magnetohydrodynamics   99
   S. CHANDRASEKHAR
   Discussion of Paper Seven   105

Paper Eight, On the Application of Numerical Methods to the
   Solution of Systems of Partial Differential Equations Aris-
   ing in Meteorology   107
   J. SMAGORINSKY
   Discussion of Paper Eight.   125

Index   127

FRONTIERS
OF NUMERICAL
MATHEMATICS

Paper One | **WILLIAM PRAGER**

Stress Analysis
in the Plastic Range

§1. Constitutive Laws

The analysis of stresses and strains in structures and machine
parts has traditionally been based on Hooke's law, which stipulates
a linear homogeneous relation between the tensors of stress and strain.
For a cylindrical or prismatic bar in simple tension or compression,
this law furnishes a straight-line diagram of axial force F versus
elongation λ (Fig. 1a). Somewhat more realistic diagrams for typical structural metals are shown in Figs. 1b and 1c: the proportionality
between force and elongation is restricted to the elastic range 0A (or
0A'), which is followed by the plastic range AB (or A'B').

Figure 1b corresponds to a perfectly plastic solid, and Fig. 1c
to a work-hardening solid. In both figures, the line OABCDB' represents the behavior under loading in tension (OAB) followed by unloading (BC) and loading in compression (CDB') . The abscissa of
the point C indicates the plastic (or permanent) elongation after complete unloading from B , and the difference between the abscissas of
B and C , the elastic (or recoverable) elongation that is recovered
during this unloading. In a perfectly plastic tension specimen, the
axial force remains constant during an increase of the plastic elongation; in a work-hardening tension specimen, however, the axial force
increases monotonically with the plastic elongation.

For mathematical simplicity, the useful portions of the work-
hardening branches AB and A'B' of the diagram showing force versus
elongation may be approximated by parallel straight lines as in Fig. 1c
(linear work-hardening). For loading from the virgin state O , the absolute value Y of the ordinates of the points A and A' in Fig. 1c
represents the yield forces in tension or compression. For loading
from the plastically prestrained state C , the corresponding yield
forces are given by the absolute values of the ordinates of B and D .
Plastic prestraining in tension thus raises the tensile yield force above
its value in the virgin state, but lowers the compressive yield force.
This is known as the Bauschinger effect.

3

Inspection of the diagrams of Figs. 1b and c reveals that in a given state F, λ of the specimen the infinitesimal increment $d\lambda$ of the elongation uniquely determines the increment dF of the force. For mathematical convenience, the relations between $d\lambda$ and dF are usually written as relations between the time rates $\dot{\lambda}$ and $\dot{F}$ of elongation and axial force. Since the solids under consideration are not supposed to exhibit any viscosity effects, these relations must be homogeneous in the time rates. Let the slope of the line OA in Figs. 1b or 1c be denoted by C , the slope of AB by c , and the intercept made by AB on the F-axis by Y^* , and let $[x]$ stand for x if $x > 0$ and for 0 if $x \le 0$. The mechanical behavior represented by the diagrams in Figs. 1b and 1c is then specified by the following constitutive law:

$$
\dot{F} = \begin{cases} C\dot{\lambda} & \text{if } (F - c\lambda)^2 < Y^{*2} \ , \\[2em] C\left\{\dot{\lambda} - \dfrac{C-c}{CY^{*2}}(F - c\lambda)[(F - c\lambda)\dot{\lambda}]\right\} & \text{if } (F-c\lambda)^2 = Y^{*2} \ . \end{cases} \tag{1}
$$

For a work-hardening solid $(c > 0)$, this constitutive law has the inverse

$$
C\dot{\lambda} = \begin{cases} \dot{F} & \text{if } (F - c\lambda)^2 < Y^{*2} \\[2em] \dot{F} + \dfrac{C-c}{cY^{*2}}(F - c\lambda)[(F - c\lambda)\dot{F}] & \text{if } (F - c\lambda)^2 = Y^{*2} \ , \end{cases} \tag{2}
$$

which furnishes a unique rate of elongation $\dot{\lambda}$, when the state F, λ and the rate of force $\dot{F}$ are given. For a perfectly plastic solid $(c = 0)$, however, the second line of (2) must be replaced by

$$
\operatorname{sgn} \dot{\lambda} = \operatorname{sgn} F \quad \text{if } (F - c\lambda)^2 = Y^{*2} \text{ and } (F - c\lambda)\dot{F} = 0 \ . \tag{3}
$$

§2. Geometrical representation of state of stress

For lack of time, we refrain from discussing the corresponding constitutive laws for three-dimensional states of stress and strain. The most widely used of these laws is due to von Mises [1] and represents perfectly plastic behavior. An up-to-date survey of laws for work-hardening as well as perfectly plastic solids has recently been given by Koiter [2].

In the following, the truss shown in Fig. 2 will be used to indicate typical problems of plastic stress analysis. The prismatic bars of the truss are connected by frictionless hinges and therefore stressed in simple tension or compression; their mechanical behavior is supposed to be described by the constitutive laws considered in Section 1. The truss is supported by fixed hinges at A and B , and by a moveable hinge at C . Initially, the truss is free from loads and the axial force in each bar vanishes. The bar forces caused by the given time-dependent vertical load P acting at the joint D are to be determined as functions of time; the load intensity is supposed to vary slowly, so that dynamic effects need not be considered.

Let F_i be the axial force in the i-th bar of the truss, and C_i the slope of the elastic branch of its force-versus-elongation diagram. The elastic strain energy associated with the bar forces F_i is given by $\Sigma F_i^2/(2C_i)$, where the summation is extended over all bars of the truss. A state of stress with unit elastic strain energy will be called a standard state.

It is convenient to regard the generic state of stress in the truss as a linear combination of two standard states. The first of these represents the purely elastic response of the considered statically indeterminate truss to a load of suitably chosen intensity P' (Fig. 2a). The bar forces F'_i of this state are computed as if all bars behaved in a purely elastic manner, and the load intensity P' is determined from the condition that the state should be standard. The second state represents a deviation from purely elastic response; its bar forces are obtained by analyzing the statically determinate truss in Fig. 2c, the intensity Q'' of the sole load being chosen to yield a standard state.

The bar forces of a generic state of stress in the elastic-plastic truss of Fig. 2a can then be written in the form

$$F_i = pF'_i + qF''_i \, , \qquad\qquad (4)$$

where p and q are measures for the intensities of the load and the deviation from purely elastic response, respectively. In the following, p will be called the load factor.

The virtual work of the force Q'' in Fig. 2c on the displacements of the elastic state in Fig. 2b vanishes. Accordingly, $\Sigma F'_i F''_i/C_i = 0$ by the principle of virtual work. The elastic strain energy $E = \Sigma F_i^2/(2C_i)$ of the state (4) can therefore be written in the form

$$E = p^2 + q^2 \, , \qquad\qquad (5)$$

where the standard character of the states F'_i and F''_i has been used.

Equation (5) suggests the use of a stress plane in which the stress point with the rectangular Cartesian coordinates p, q represents the state of stress (4). According to (5) the elastic strain energy of this state is given by the square of the distance of the stress point from the origin.

§3. Perfectly plastic truss

Consider first a truss all bars of which are perfectly plastic, and denote the yield force of the i-th bar by Y_i . As the absolute value of the axial force (4) in this bar cannot exceed Y_i ,

$$-Y_i \leq pF'_i + qF''_i \leq Y_i \, . \qquad\qquad (6)$$

The points p, q of the stress plane that satisfy (6) fill a strip which will be called the <u>yield strip</u> of the i-th bar. The boundaries of this strip are symmetrically situated with respect to the origin 0 of the stress plane.

The convex region common to the yield strips of all bars is bounded by the <u>yield polygon.</u> For a stress point outside the yield polygon, the absolute value of the axial force in at least one bar would exceed the yield force of this bar. These stress points can therefore be disregarded. For the purposes of the following qualitative discussion it will be assumed that the yield polygon has the shape indicated in Fig. 3.

The origin 0 in Fig. 3 represents the stress-free state. If, starting from this state, the load factor is slowly increased, the truss behaves at first in a completely elastic manner, that is, the load point moves in the positive p direction. At 1 the stress point reaches a side of the yield polygon, which has been labeled j^+ to indicate that it corresponds to $F_j = Y_j$. At the load factor represented by the abscissa of 1 , the j-th bar therefore reaches its tensile yield force. As the load factor continues to increase, this bar stretches plastically under the constant force $F_j = Y_j$, that is, the stress point moves along the side j^+ towards the upper right.

At 2 , the stress point reaches the side k^- of the yield polygon, which corresponds to $F_k = -Y_k$. As the load factor continues to increase, the stress point leaves the boundary j^+ of the j-th yield strip and moves along the boundary k^- of the k-th yield strip into the interior of the j-th yield strip. This means that the j-th bar stops yielding in tension as soon as the k-th bar starts yielding in compression. We have here one of the many surprises plastic structures have in store for the analyst who has only dealt with elastic structures: <u>monotonically increasing loads do not imply monotonically increasing stresses</u>.

For a given value p_0 of the load factor, the line $p = p_0$ will be called the <u>line of equilibrium</u> because its points represent states of stress that are in equilibrium with the loads corresponding to the considered value of the load factor. While the stress point describes the path $0-1-2-3-4$ in Fig. 3, it is seen to be that point of the instantaneous line of equilibrium which is closest to the origin without falling outside the yield polygon. In mechanical terms: <u>for monotonically increasing load, the state of stress is that equilibrium state for the instantaneous loads which minimizes the elastic strain energy without involving stresses beyond the yield limit.</u>

Haar and von Kármán [3] stipulated this principle as the basis of their theory of perfectly plastic solids. Henky [4] derived the corresponding constitutive law, which, however, does not satisfy certain physical requirements. * The principle of Haar and von Kármán can, however, be proved for a physically acceptable constitutive law under the restricting assumption that, at any point where the yield limit is reached, the state of stress remains constant during the subsequent loading process. While this condition is sufficient for the validity

of the principle, it is obviously not necessary, because for the truss
considered here, the principle remains valid although the force in the
j-th bar drops below the yield limit while the stress point moves from
2 to 4. A necessary and sufficient condition for the validity of the
principle of Haar and von Kármán has not yet been established.

For a truss, the principle of Haar and von Kármán would reduce
the analysis of the stresses under monotonically increasing loads to
a problem in quadratic programming: a positive definite quadratic form
(the elastic strain energy) is to be minimized subject to constraints
that consist of linear equations (expressing the equilibrium between
bar forces and the loads at each joint of the truss) and linear inequalities (stating that the stress in a generic bar cannot sink below the
compressive yield limit or rise above the tensile yield limit). The
SHARE code for linear programming on the IBM 704 has recently been
modified to apply to problems of this kind [6].

The load factor given by the abscissa of point 4 in Fig. 3 indicates
the load carrying capacity of the truss: any equilibrium state that corresponds to a greater load factor would involve stresses beyond the
yield limit. The load carrying capacity and the corresponding limiting
state of stress can be found by determining that supporting line of the
convex yield polygon which is normal to the p axis. This is obviously a linear programming problem: p is to be maximized subject to inequalities of the form (6). Dorn and Greenberg [7] have recently discussed the load carrying capacity of trusses from this point of view;
earlier, Greenberg, Prager, and Drucker [8] had given a statical maximum characterization and a kinematical minimum characterization of
the load carrying capacity of a perfectly plastic structure. Some of
their results seem to have been anticipated in a rare Russian publication [9]. In view of the well-known duality between the statical and
the kinematical approach in theory of structures, it is not surprising
that the complementary extremum principles of Greenberg, Prager and
Drucker lead to dual linear programming problems. Formal proofs of
this were given by Charnes and Greenberg [10] for trusses and by
Charnes, Lemke, and Zienkiewicz [11] for beams and frames.

Dropping the assumption of monotonically increasing loads, suppose that the load factor is reduced after it has reached the value represented by the abscissa of the point 2 in Fig. 3. Since unloading is
essentially an elastic process, the stress point will move along the
parallel 2-5 to the p axis. The point 5 , which has the abscissa
zero, represents the residual state of stress after complete unloading
from 2.

Under monotonically increasing load, the principle of Haar and
von Kármán relates the state of stress directly to the state of loading.
When unloading is admitted, any attempt at establishing such a direct
relation is doomed to fail. The "integral" principle of Haar and von
Kármán is then replaced by the "differential" principle of Greenberg
[12], which considers the states of stress and loading as given and
establishes a relation between their infinitesimal changes. In the
geometrical terminology appropriate for Fig. 3, Greenberg's principle

can be expressed as follows: as the line of equilibrium performs an infinitesimal translation in accordance with a given infinitesimal change of the load factor, the stress point undergoes the smallest displacement compatible with the conditions that it must remain on the line of equilibrium and cannot move outside the yield polygon.

After complete unloading from 2, let the truss be loaded in the opposite sense, i.e. by an upward vertical load acting at the joint D in Fig. 2a . As the intensity of this load is increased, the stress point moves from 5 on a parallel to the p axis to the left (Fig. 3) until it reaches the side j^- of the yield polygon at 6 . The j-th bar now begins to yield in compression and the stress point moves along the side j^- to the lower left. If the sense of loading is reversed at 7 , the stress point moves along the p axis to the right. If the load factor oscillates between the values represented by the abscissas of 2 and 7 , the stress point describes the closed path 2-6-7-1-2 for each cycle of loading, the segment 1-2 of this path corresponding to tensile yielding of the j-th bar and the segment 6-7 to compressive yielding of the same bar. Since a bar cannot withstand an indefinite number of such cycles of plastic deformation the truss will fail under the considered cycles of load.

If the load factor oscillates between the values represented by the abscissas of the points 3 and 9, each cycle of loading is represented by the loop 3-8-9-10-3, the segments 10-3 and 8-9 of which correspond to compressive yielding of the k-th bar and tensile yielding of the m-th bar, respectively. These repeated plastic contractions of the k-th bar and plastic extensions of the m-th bar are likely to lead to unacceptable deformations of the truss. For practical purposes, the truss must therefore be regarded as failing under the cycles of loading considered here.

If, on the other hand, the load factor oscillates between the values represented by the abscissas of 2 and 6, the j-th bar yields in tension during the part 1-2 of the first loading 0-1-2, but the subsequent cycles of loading 2-6-2 do not involve any further plastic deformation: an initial plastic deformation enables the truss to shake down to a state of residual stress (represented by 5) in which it reacts in a purely elastic manner to all further cycles of loading.

The possibility of failure by alternating plastic flow was first discussed by Bleich [13] for simply indeterminate structures only, and more generally by Melan [14]; the possibility of failure by progressive plastic flow was pointed out more recently by Horne [15]. Bleich and Melan also gave a criterion characterizing those cycles of loading under which a perfectly plastic structure will shake down. In the geometric language appropriate to Fig. 3, this criterion can be stated as follows. The purely elastic response to the considered cycles of loading would be represented by the segment 2' – 6' of the p axis. As this contains points outside the yield polygon, these cycles must at least involve some initial plastic deformation. The truss will however shake down if this segment can be given a translation normal to the p axis which will not leave any of its points outside the yield polygon.

Without going into details, we mention the corresponding criterion for trusses with several degrees of redundancy under states of loading that are characterized by several independently varying load factors. The purely elastic response to a considered convex set of states of loading is then represented by a convex polyhedron in the elastic subspace of stress space. Shake down will occur if and only if this polyhedron can be given a translation normal to this subspace that will not leave any of its points outside the convex yield polyhedron. Neal and Symonds [16] have shown how this kind of problem can be treated for perfectly plastic structures of moderate size, but their method requires a good deal of ingenuity and could not readily be used on a computer.

To save time, the preceding discussion was restricted to the iso-thermal deformations of a simply indeterminate truss. Thermal effects are treated in [17] and the generalization to trusses of higher degrees of redundancy, and to beams and frames in [18, Chapter 2], where further literature references will be found.

The preceding remarks were exclusively concerned with the analy-sis of a given perfectly plastic structure. For lack of time, we can but briefly mention the challenging problem of designing a perfectly plastic structure so that it withstands a given set of states of loading while employing a minimum amount of structural material. For trusses, beams and frames, this problem can be reduced to one in linear programming, but when the simplex method is used even frames of moderate numbers of bays and stories may tax the capacity of the largest computers currently available. A somewhat more efficient method has recently been developed by Heyman and Prager [19]; it was coded for the IBM 704 by Kalker [20] and for the IBM 650 by Stone [21].

§4. Work-hardening truss

Whereas a variety of problem types have been identified for perfectly plastic structures and general principles have been established for their treatment, few similarly general results are available for work-hardening structures.

To indicate some of the difficulties, let all bars of the truss in Fig. 2 be linearly work-hardening and denote the yield force in the virgin state of the i-th bar (the ordinate of A in Fig. 1c) by Y_i , and the slopes of the elastic and work-hardening branches of its force-versus-elongation diagram by C_i and c_i , respectively, and set $K_i = C_i c_i / (C_i - c_i)$. The continued inequality (6) then specifies the yield strip of the i-th bar only in the virgin state. If, however, the i-th bar has experienced a plastic elongation λ_i^* (e.g. the one represented by OC in Fig. 1c) its yield forces in tension (ordinate of B) and compression (absolute value of ordinate of D) are found to be $Y_i + K_i \lambda_i^*$ and $Y_i - K_i \lambda_i^*$, respectively. The corresponding yield strip is specified by

$$-Y_i + K_i \lambda_i^* \leq pF'_i + qF''_i \leq Y_i + K_i \lambda_i^* . \tag{7}$$

When the plastic elongations of all bars are known, their yield strips can be determined; the convex region common to these strips is the <u>yield polygon,</u> which therefore depends on the state of plastic deformation of the truss. Let the full-line polygon in Fig. 4 be the yield polygon for the virgin state of the truss. If, starting from this state, the truss is subjected to a monotonically increasing load, the stress point moves at first along the p axis until it reaches the yield polygon at 1 . Since this point lies on the side j^+ of the yield polygon, the j-th bar starts yielding in tension, while all other bars continue to behave elastically. During this phase the increment of the elongation of any bar is proportional to the increment of the force in this bar. The direction of the path of the stress point during this phase can therefore be found from an elastic analysis in which the elastic constant C_j of the j-th bar must however be replaced by its work-hardening constant c_j . Referring the reader to a paper by Ziegler [22] for details, we only remark that this direction must lie between the positive p direction and the direction 1-A (Fig. 4), which correspond to perfectly elastic behavior $(c_j = C_j)$ and perfectly plastic behavior $(c_j = 0)$, respectively.

In Fig. 4, let 1-2 be the path of the stress point when the j-th bar yields in tension while all other bars behave elastically. As the stress point moves along 1-2, the yield strip of the j-th bar undergoes a translation such that its right-hand boundary always contains the instantaneous stress point. As long as the other bars behave elastically, their yield strips remain fixed. When the stress point reaches the position 2, the sides j^+ and j^- of the original yield polygon are therefore replaced by the sides B-2 and B'-2' ; the sides k^+ and m^+ are shortened by corresponding amounts.

Since the point 2 lies on k^- , the k-th bar now begins to yield in compression, and the direction of motion of the stress point changes, because the elastic constant C_k of this bar must now be replaced by its work-hardening constant c_k .

The point 3 in Fig. 4 lies on the line n^+ , which corresponds to tensile yielding of the n-th bar. When the stress point reaches the position 3, the sides j^+ and k^- of the original yield polygon are replaced by C-3 and D-3, respectively, and the sides j^- and k^+ by C'-3' and D'-3' .

As this discussion shows, the stress history of the truss is a sequence of quasi-elastic phases, during each of which force and elongation of a typical bar increase in proportion, the factor of proportionality being either the elastic or the work-hardening constant of the bar according to whether the bar behaves elastically or yields. Which bars are behaving elastically and which are yielding during a phase is determined by the state of stress at the end of the preceding phase.

It follows from these remarks that the extremum principles of classical elasticity can be modified to characterize the rates of stress or strain in a work-hardening structure when the instantaneous stresses and strains are known and the rate of loading is prescribed. The extremum principle for the stress rates is essentially due to Hodge and

Prager [23] and that for strain rates to Greenberg [12]. These principles reduce the analysis of a work-hardening structure to a problem in
differential quadratic programming.

If the yield limits of the bars could be raised indefinitely by work-
hardening, the truss could carry a load of arbitrary intensity. Actually,
rupture occurs when the force reaches a critical value. When a bar
fails in this manner, the degree of redundancy of the truss is reduced
by one, and the forces in the remaining bars change discontinuously.
If the new forces do not exceed the limits of rupture of the bars, a further increase in the load intensity is possible; otherwise the rupture
of the first bar causes other bars to fail, and the load carrying capacity of the truss is reached. While Ziegler [22] has discussed this effect for a particular truss, general theorems characterizing the load
carrying capacity under these assumptions have not yet been established. The corresponding effect for perfectly plastic trusses was investigated by Erim and Yüksel [24].

Shake down of a truss with linearly work-hardening members was
discussed by Melan [25] and Neal [26]. Expressed in the geometric
terms appropriate to Fig. 4, Melan's result is as follows. Consider
the segment of the p axis that represents the purely elastic response
to the given variation of the load intensity. If the virgin yield strips
of the bars of the truss can be given such translations that this segment lies in their common region, the truss will shake down. #

§5. Conclusions

We have illustrated typical problems of plastic stress analysis by
using as example a truss, in which the state of stress can be specified
by the values of a finite number of parameters. For this discrete model,
linear programming, quadratic programming, and differential quadratic
programming turned out to be important tools of plastic stress analysis.
In discs, plates, and shells, however, and in the three-dimensional
continuum, the state of stress is specified by functions of position.
While extremum characterizations of the state of stress have been giv-
en and individual problems have been solved for these continuous models, efficient methods of plastic stress analysis have yet to be developed. In view of the complexity of the problem, there can be no doubt
that these methods will have to be numerical rather than analytical.
The papers listed under [28], which employ the finite difference approach , illustrate the difficulties arising from the following circumstances: the stress analysis must be carried out not for a single state
of loading as in the corresponding elastic problem but for a sequence
of states of loading, and different relations apply in the elastic and
plastic regions, the interface of which changes with the state of
loading.

NOTES

* For a general critique of constitutive laws of this type, see [5].

For restrictions on the validity of this theorem, see [27].

REFERENCES

1. R. von Mises, Mechanik fester Körper im plastisch deformablen Zustand, Göttinger Nachrichten, math.-phys. Kl. (1913) 582.

2. W. T. Koiter, General theorems for elastic-plastic solids, in press.

3. A. Haar and T. von Kármán, Zur Theorie der Spannungszustände in plastischen und sandartigen Medien, Göttinger Nachrichten, math. phys. Kl. (1909) 204.

4. H. Hencky, Zur Theorie plastischer Deformationen und der hierdurch im Material hervorgerufenen Nachspannungen, Zeitschrift angew. Math. Mech. 4 (1924) 323.

5. G. H. Handelman, C. C. Lin, and W. Prager, On the mechanical behaviour of metals in the strain-hardening range, Quarterly Appl. Math. 4 (1947) 397-407.

6. P. Wolfe, The simplex method for quadratic programming, The Rand Corp., Research Memorandum No. 2388 (1959).

7. W. Dorn and H. J. Greenberg, Linear programming and plastic limit analysis of structures, Quarterly Appl. Math. 15 (1957) 155.

8. H. J. Greenberg and W. Prager, On limit design of beams and frames, Brown University, Technical Report No. A 18-1, Providence, R.I., 1949 = Trans. Amer. Soc. Civil Engrs. 117 91952) 447 (with discussion); D. C. Drucker, W. Prager, and H. J. Greenberg, Extended limit design theorems for continuous media, Quarterly Appl. Math. 9 (1952) 381; W. Prager, The general theory of limit design, General Lecture, 8th Internat. Congress Theor. and Appl. Mech. (Istanbul, 1952), Proceedings, vol. 2, Istanbul 1955, p. 65.

9. A. A. Gvozdev, The determination of the value of the collapse loads for statically indeterminate systems undergoing plastic deformation, Proc. Conf. Plastic Deformation, Akad. Nauk USSR, 1938, p. 19.

10. A. Charnes and H. J. Greenberg, unpublished paper, an abstract of which appeared in Bull. Amer. Math. Soc. 57 (1951) 480.

11. A. Charnes, C. E. Lemke, and O. C. Zienkiewicz, Virtual work, linear programming and plastic limit analysis, Proc. Roy. Soc. (A) 251 (1959) 110.

12. H. J. Greenberg, Complementary minimum principles for an elastic-plastic material, Quarterly Appl. Math. 7 (1949) 85.

13. H. Bleich, Über die Bemessung statisch unbestimmter Stahltragwerke unter Berücksichtigung des elastisch-plastischen Verhaltens des Baustoffes, Bauingenieur 19/20 (1932), 261.

14. E. Melan, Theorie statisch unbestimmter Stahltragwerke aus ideal-plastischem Baustoff, Sitz. Ber. Akad. Wiss. Wien, (IIa) 145 (1936) 195.

15. M. R. Horne, Fundamental propositions in plastic theory of structures, Journal Instn. Civ. Engrs. 34 (1950) 174.

16. P. S. Symonds and B. G. Neal, The calculation of failure loads on plane frames under arbitrary loading programmes, Journal Instn. Civil Engrs. 35 (1950) 41.

17. W. Prager, Plastic design and thermal stresses, British Welding Journal 3 (1956) 355.

18. W. Prager, An introduction to plasticity, Addison-Wesley Publishing Co., Reading, Mass., 1959.

19. J. Heyman and W. Prager, Automatic minimum weight design of steel frames, Journal Franklin Inst. 266 (1958) 339.

20. J. Kalker, Automatic minimum weight design of steel frames on the IBM 704 computer, Brown University, Report IBM 2038/3 (1958).

21. R. L. Stone, Automatic minimum weight design of steel frames on the IBM 650 computer, Brown University, Report IBM 2038/4 (1958).

22. H. Ziegler, Redundant trusses of elastic, strain-hardening material, Journal Appl. Mech. 25 (1958) 233.

23. P. G. Hodge, Jr. and W. Prager, A variational principle for plastic materials with strain-hardening, Journal Math. Phys. 27 (1948).

24. K. Erim and H. Yüksel, Some remarks on elastic-plastic trusses, Proc. 8th Internat. Congress Theoret. and Appl. Mech. (Istanbul 1952) vol. 1, Istanbul, 1943, p. 230.

25. E. Melan, Theorie statisch unbestimmter Systeme, Prelim. Publ. 2nd Congress, Internat. Assoc. Bridge and Structural Engg., Berlin, 1936, p. 45.

26. B. G. Neal, Plastic collapse and shake down theorems for structures of strain-hardening material, Journal Aeron. Sci. 17 (1950) 297.

27. W. T. Koiter, Some remarks on plastic shake down theorems, Proc. 8th Internat. Congress Theoret. Appl. Mech. (Istanbul 1952) vol. 1, Istanbul, 1953, p. 220.

28. R. P. Eddy and F. S. Shaw, Numerical solution of elastoplastic torsion of a shaft of rotational symmetry, Journal Appl. Mech. 16 (1949) 139; D. N. de G. Allen and R. V. Southwell, Plastic straining in two-dimensional stress systems, Phil. Trans. Roy. Soc. London (A) 242 (1950) 379; J. A. Jacobs, Relaxation methods applied to plastic flow, Phil. Mag. (7) 41 (1950) 458.

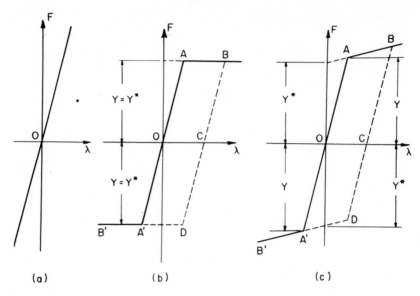

Fig. 1

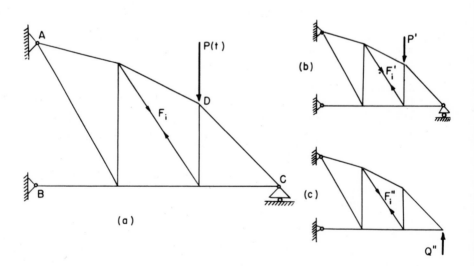

Fig. 2

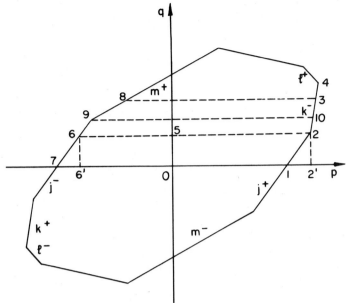

Fig. 3

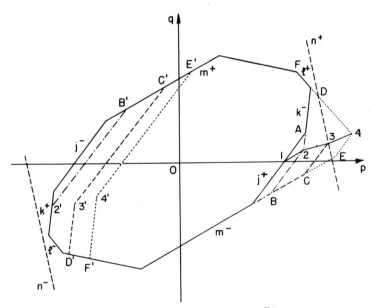

Fig. 4

Discussion of Paper One

Dr. Smagorinsky: You spoke of differential quadratic programming. I wonder whether one could assume that for small enough differential steps that one could replace this by linear programming?

Dr. Prager: No, (see Fig. 3)—as a matter of fact, the stress point describes the shortest path compatible with the conditions that it should always be on the instantaneous line of equilibrium and never more outside the yield polygon, shortest in the ordinary quadratic line element sense; this is where the quadratic character comes in even though you deal with differentials. It is $dp^2 + dq^2$ that you want to minimize subject to those conditions— dp, in fact, is given because you want to know what is done to the load, and you want to determine dq such that $dp^2 + dq^2$ is minimum subject to all these continued inequalities.

Dr. Birkhoff: I wonder, in view of what you said, if this is perhaps a little like what happens when you pass to the limit with Brownian motions. Everything becomes singular, and the velocities become infinite because you have $dp^2 + dq^2$ is related to a linear quantity. That means that it decreases like a square root, which is what happens in Brownian movement, and therefore you cannot just linearize in the limit ... you have to proceed quite differently.

Dr. Prager: Yes, you could sort of pseudo-linearize as you pointed out, by taking the square root, but that doesn't make it linear in the sense of linear programming.

Dr. Lieberstein: I would like to ask you to comment on the role you think numerical analysis should play in the dynamic aspects of plasticity. Specifically, do you think stress-strain relations, having higher orders smooth derivatives should be determined at high loading rates; and, next, do you think we could hope to solve three-dimensional problems under impact conditions in the near future?

Dr. Prager: Some of these peculiarities of behavior obviously come from the fact that our stress-strain diagram has a sharp break (elastic-plastic). Some sixteen to seventeen years ago I was very hopeful that by introducing stress-strain relations which show a continuous transition from elastic to plastic behavior, one might take to simplify this. This has not been borne out by the facts. The best analysis one can give today—the simplest analysis—is still based on this elastic-plastic behavior which I showed here. The trouble is this. You might smooth out the ascending part of the curve like that, but once you have come to this and unloaded, this line has to be the realistic parallel to the initial tangent of the curve, so here is a sharp bend that you cannot

possibly avoid if you want to be realistic physically. Even the simple examples considered here show that individual bars may stop
yielding when the load keeps increasing monotonically, so you always
must allow for this sort of thing, and there is your trouble back. That's
why these smooth laws have not proved to be more easy for purposes of
numerical analysis than the usual law where you have a discontinuity
in the slope.

Dr. Rosen: In your discussion you considered a simple case for
purposes of illustration. You were able to represent this as a convex
region in the two-dimensional space of the variables p and q . How
general a problem can be represented by a two-dimensional region and
to what extent can these problems be generalized in terms of a convex
region in a higher dimensional space?

Dr. Prager: In the two-dimensional space this is about as general as you can be. In a three-dimensional space, you can look into
various things; for instance, you may have two redundancies and a
one-parameter system of loads, or you may have one redundancy and
a two-parameter system of loads, and both cases give very interesting
results. And, of course, you can—in words anyhow—generalize to an
n-dimensional Euclidean space where you have any number of redundancies and any number of load parameters. In our simple example,
the two states which we described by prime and double-prime proved
to be orthogonal in the sense that the pq term disappears from our
strain energy expression, but in the other case, you must deliberately
orthonormalize the states of stress you use to represent the generic
bar force by a linear combination of those states of stress; once you
have carried out this orthonormalization processs, the discussion becomes almost as simple as the one given here and the problem still
can be handled as a quadratic programming problem on a computer.

Dr. Lieberstein: I don't want to change the topic, but there is
something we wanted to ask you about. At Aberdeen some very high
speed pellets have been fired into clear plastic, and the shock apparently—not just the sonic disturbance which is usually seen in elasticity—has been photographed travelling through the median. To me
this is a new phenomenon in plasticity, and I was wondering if you
care to comment.

Dr. Prager: Is the plastic "plastic" in the sense I use the word?
It's probably brittle, isn't it?

Dr. Lieberstein: Under the impact conditions, I'm certain viscosity would come in, too.

Dr. Prager: Viscosity would come in, yes. But, what you call
"shock", it's not actual rupture, is it?

Dr. Lieberstein: There's no rupture in the material. You don't
see any effect except the penetration of the pellet, but you can watch
a spherical discontinuity travelling through the material. It's bright,
but I think that's optical. It's travelling faster than sonic speed.

Dr. Prager: Is the material highly compressible, or is it almost
incompressible?

Dr. Lieberstein: Well, it's solid. . .

Dr. Prager: It's solid, certainly, but it could be incompressible as a solid having the Poisson ratio one-half. I think that what you probably refer to is a density change which you see optically and which would point to a compressible material. It might be interesting to expose a cube or sphere of your plastic statically to a very high pressure—a Bridgeman order of pressures. You will probably have to wrap it in tinfoil so you don't get pressure into pores if it has any pores, because that would explode it, and see how the volume changes...whether you get appreciable volume change under high pressures. If "yes", then I think the answer is that the discontinuity you see is a discontinuity in density.

Dr. Bueckner: Can you generalize all of this for trusses which have friction at the joints of the bars...

Dr. Prager: ...trusses where the bar forces need no longer be acting in the geometrical axis of the bar...what would you want to specify about the friction?

Dr. Bueckner: What I'm asking is, could you by this technique approximate a continuous part by a truss?

Dr. Prager: This is a very interesting question, but I wouldn't dare answer it without giving it much more thought than I could now. There is, of course, even with the ideal truss a very well-known technique in elasticity where you take a truss which is build like this..., as a discontinuous or discrete analog to the elastic two-

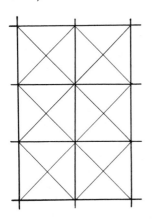

dimensional continuum. You must determine the ratio between the elastic moduli of the bars which form the squares and the bars which form the diagonals so that the response of a large glob of this material is quasi-isotropic. That has been done, and I think it would be good for computer people to look back to this because the last attempt along these lines, as far as I know, was made back in the early 1930's when the present powerful computers were not available. It was then found that in order to get with this sort of analysis anything which would sufficiently closely describe the continuum, the requisite number of squares was so high it was just completely beyond all possibilities of desk computers. It might be worthwhile to look at this again and see whether it is still beyond the range of presently available computers. And one could, of course, extend that in principle to two-dimensional analog of the plastic continuum. We have thought about that but have not done anything about it. You see, there is one thing which bothers me in this case a little bit. You would want to say that a certain point of the continuum is either plastic or elastic, but some of the bars which radiate from this point might be plastic and others may still be elastic. Was this point in the elastic domain or the plastic domain? Do you call plastic domain everything where at least one point—one bar—is in the plastic domain? There are certain obvious difficulties which we haven't been able to straighten out in our own minds, so we haven't rushed into a computer program.

Dr. Hodge: You mentioned the very great difficulties involved in the continuum problem because you have an elastic-plastic boundary whose position, in general, you don't know. Now, if you are not concerned with a detailed analysis but only in finding the limiting plastic loads that a perfectly plastic material can carry, then of course many problems which are elastically difficult become plastically relatively easy. Essentially the reason for the simplification is that you are no longer looking for the solution to the entire problem, but only to a solution of part of it, for example the stress part of it which in turn means there is more than one possible solution available. Now, all of this makes hand work without even having to use a desk computer very much simpler, of course, but I should imagine that you would encounter situations which are not encountered in other fields if you tried to take advantage of some of this simplicity for a high speed computer. I wonder if you would give some thought to this problem.

Dr. Prager: You mean that plastic limit analysis in the continuum?

Dr. Hodge: Yes, where you are trying to find a statically admissible stress field which is not necessarily unique. Is there any efficient way of trying to find such a field by a systematic numerical procedure?

Dr. Prager: Yes, if you want to approach the corresponding elastic problem, you would probably start from a normalized set of statically admissible states of stress and combine these so as to minimize strain energy or something like that, and in the present problem you would want to combine these so that the yield limit is nowhere exceeded and that your load limit gets as high as possible. I think that could be done on a computer. Again, you would essentially deal with a discrete problem. You would look at the state of stress at the points of some space lattice rather than continuously. (See Fig. 3) This is of course what Professor Hodge is referring to—the point 4 on the diagram—the right-most point which has the largest abscissa on this convex area. This can be determined by linear programming, and the simplifications to which Professor Hodge referred arise precisely from this step from a quadratic to a linear programming program.

You will remember that we spoke of shake-down. . . if the extreme load intensities to which the structure is to be submitted varies between the abscissa of the points 3 and 8 respectively, then in the first loading we have plastic deformation, but thereafter we have purely elastic response to any further cycles of loading. The only question of course, and a very important question for the engineer, is to characterize extreme values of the load intensity such that this shake-down takes place? And you can almost for this case read it off the figure. If we had a purely elastic response, we would go along from this point on the p-axis to a point over here, but the line segment 3-8 of the p-axis sticks out of the yield polygon. If you give it an appropriate translation in the positive q sense you can move it inside the yield polygon. In general, in the n-dimensional Euclidean stress space, you have a yield polyhedron, and since we have in general not a single load parameter but a number of load parameters, instead of a p-axis we have a linear subspace of purely elastic responses, and the given extreme values of the load specify in this subspace of purely elastic responses a convex polygon, and if you can give to this convex polygon a translation normal to the subspace of purely elastic responses in such a manner that you move all the vertices of this convex polygon inside the yield polyhedron, then the structure shakes down and if you cannot do this it will not shake down.

Paper Two | **GARRETT BIRKHOFF**

Some Mathematical Problems
of Nuclear Reactor Theory

It would indeed be presumptuous to attempt to survey the mathematical problems of nuclear reactor theory in one hour; these problems involve most of the major branches of mathematics, physics, and engineering science! I shall only be able to indicate a few problems[1] very superficially. My hope is that my somewhat scattered remarks may help to stimulate interest in a new and challenging area of applied mathematics, with special reference to problems in numerical analysis.

Anyone wishing to follow up these indications by serious mathematical research should consult Ref. 1, in which a number of experts have treated various special topics, more thoroughly and with valuable bibliographies. Since five of the papers in Ref. 1 specifically concern computing techniques, covering fairly adequately what is known about at least this aspect of reactor theory, those numerical analysts who find my remarks interesting should have little difficulty in reaching the frontiers of knowledge. To advance these frontiers may be more difficult!

I. PHYSICAL BACKGROUND

§1. <u>The neutron life cycle</u>. Most nuclear reactors currently producing useful atomic power are so-called <u>thermal reactors</u>, in which nuclear fissions are mainly caused by "thermal neutrons" having energies of less than 0.1 ev. (velocities less than 5 km/sec.). In such reactors, the neutron life cycle involves some dimensional constants, whose order of magnitude should be kept in mind.

"Fission neutrons" freshly produced in nuclear fission have energies of 10^6 ev or more "at birth". They must therefore be slowed down to less than one-thousandth of their initial velocity before causing fission. This fact makes a typical neutron life cycle fairly eventful.

For example, consider an idealized homogeneous thermal reactor, consisting of a homogeneous solution of (say) uranyl sulfate in water.

In such a reactor, a fission neutron would have to collide about 20 times with hydrogen nuclei before slowing down to thermal velocities, and it might undergo 100 further collisions before causing a fresh U^{235} nucleus to fission. This would all happen in about 10^{-4} secs, and one can readily see that to calculate the mathematical expectations involved, in terms of the basic probabilities of collision and scattering in space and time, would be extremely difficult. (To describe all neutron life histories individually would be out of the question; though sampling such life-histories by "Monte Carlo" methods is often helpful; see §14.)

Yet in principle, the physical laws which determine the development of neutron chain reactions rest on simple and well-established concepts. In the main, neutrons are scattered, slowed down, and absorbed with or without fission, following known statistical laws. These laws can be simply visualized by thinking of each atomic nucleus as having known (microscopic) cross-sections[2] $\sigma_s(v)$, $\sigma_a(v)$, and $\sigma_f(v)$ for scattering, absorption without fission, and nuclear fission, respectively, such that the reaction named is produced if an idealized point neutron with velocity v passes through a sphere centered in the nucleus, and having this cross-section area.

If one assumes that atomic nuclei are randomly distributed in space, then one can deduce from the given microscopic cross-sections macroscopic cross-sections $\Sigma_s(v)$, $\Sigma_a(v)$ and $\Sigma_f(v)$, describing the probability (per unit length of travel) that a neutron will undergo a given kind of reaction. In principle, these cross-sections determine a fission-to-fission migration kernel $K(\underline{x}, \underline{y})$, describing the probability (per unit volume) that a neutron "born" at $\underline{y}$ should cause a fission at $\underline{x}$ when it "dies".

The mathematical determination of $K(\underline{x}, \underline{y})$ from cross-section data is one of the outstanding long-range problems of nuclear reactor theory; see §3. It is extremely difficult, partly because so many collisions are involved, and partly because the probability $\Sigma_a(v)$ of absorption by (say) U^{238} nuclei increases by a factor of a thousand in certain narrow resonance bands.

Resonance absorption. The interpretation of this resonance absorption is a subtle art, centering around the so-called Breit-Wigner formula; it is understood only by physicists. Conceivably, this art can be advanced by a suitable application of numerical analysis, but it is very complicated (see Refs. 2, 3). I will therefore assume below that all cross-sections have been smoothed, the resonance escape probability having been calculated by some obliging physicist.

§2. Criticality. One of the most important constants in nuclear reactor theory is the average neutron yield v per fission. This is about 2.43 for U^{235} , in thermal reactors. After allowing for the loss of neutrons by resonance absorption and leakage (escape), the migration kernel $K(\underline{x},\underline{y})$ determines from this v the multiplication factor $k < v$, or ratio of the expected number of neutrons in successive generations. If $k < 1$, the reactor is said to be subcritical, if $k = 1$, it is said to be <u>critical</u>; and if $k > 1$, it is called <u>super-critical</u>.

Since the mean lifetime ℓ^* of neutrons is less than a tenth of a millisecond in most reactors, it is clear that a reactor must be very nearly critical to be a stable source of power. At first sight, one might exaggerate the implications of this fact, and suppose it necessary to maintain k in the range $.9999 < k < 1.0001$ to prevent power oscillations from exceeding 10% (say). But such stringency is not necessary, largely because of a quite special physical phenomenon: the existence of delayed neutrons. Whereas the life of most neutrons in a typical nuclear reactor is only a fraction of a millisecond, a small fraction of the fission fragments (e.g., Kr^{87}, Kr^{88}, Xe^{137}, Xe^{138}) remain in an excited state for a half-second up to a minute before producing neutrons. About 0.64% of all neutrons are produced in this way. Neutrons produced after this lapse of time are called <u>delayed neutrons</u>; their existence makes the engineering problem of stabilizing reactors much easier, and the mathematical problem of calculating time-dependent reactor behavior much harder.

The delayed neutron fraction makes it sufficient to keep k in the range $.995 < k < 1.005$. When $k > 1.0064$, a reactor is said to be "prompt critical", because there are enough "prompt" or undelayed neutrons to make the reactor supercritical, so that the flux and power levels may increase with dangerous rapidity.

Because of this limitation, most reactor calculations are limited to the range of k just specified.

<u>Reactor components</u>. Physically, most power reactors are not homogeneous but <u>heterogeneous</u>: typically, they are complicated assemblies of <u>fuel rods</u> or plates of fissionable material, and movable <u>control rods</u> containing boron or cadmium (which absorb neutrons). Between these lie channels filled with <u>coolant</u> water to convey thermal energy; this also acts as a <u>moderator</u> to slow down neutrons to the thermal range. This assembly may be surrounded by a <u>reflector</u> to prevent neutrons from leaking out, and also shielded to absorb lethal radiation.

As a result of this complicated geometry, whereas criticality can often be estimated for homogeneous reactors by analytical methods, modern high-speed digital computing machines are almost indispensible if one wishes to estimate <u>a priori</u> the <u>criticality</u> of heterogeneous reactors.

II. MATHEMATICAL MODELS

§3. <u>Transport theory</u>. As in other branches of "applied mathematics", the mathematical theory of nuclear reactors is based on simplified models, which are only able to represent physical reality approximately. The best such model is provided by so-called <u>transport theory</u>.

This model is mathematically like those assumed in the kinetic theory of gases, in the theory of radiation transfer, and other branches of statistical mechanics. In principle, it assumes that neutrons are slowed down ("moderated") and scattered by successive collisions with individual nuclei[3], and also captured by fissionable nuclei, according to specific statistical laws of the type described in §1. Thus it assumes that neutron behavior can be treated as a generalized stochastic process[4].

The usual analytical formulations of transport theory are in terms of extremely complicated Boltzmann equations. I shall not even write these down[5]; I shall simply describe them qualitatively, and mention some important problems to which they lead.

The Boltzman equations take the expected neutron density $N(\underline{x}, \underline{u}; t)$ at position $\underline{x}$, velocity $\underline{u}$, and time t, as the function to be determined from the initial density $N(\underline{x}, \underline{u}; 0)$ and the reactor geometry. Since most scattering collisions are elastic, and the laws and cross-sections for elastic scattering are known experimentally, one can formulate a basic mathematical problem of reactor theory as follows.

First Problem. Given smoothed cross-section and scattering laws for the components of a reactor, calculate the migration kernel $K(\underline{x}, \underline{y}, t)$ which describes the probability (per unit volume and time) that a fission neutron produced at $\underline{y}$ with velocity v will undergo fission capture at $\underline{x}$, t seconds later.

In Part III, we will describe how the spatial migration kernel $K(\underline{x}, \underline{y}) = \int_0^\infty K(\underline{x}, y, t) dt$, and the neutron yield ν , together determine the multiplication factor k . But it should be emphasized that existing transport calculations refer to models which have been highly simplified.

Most transport calculations treat only one-dimensional problems having slab, cylindrical or spherical symmetry[6], and even this case is complicated enough (see §11). In fact, most of the available literature simplifies the problem still further, by assuming that all neutrons have the same energy: that is, by considering hypothetical monoenergetic neutrons. This drastic assumption, which ignores the important phenomenon of neutron slowing down entirely, may be approximately applicable to thermal neutrons. At any rate, it makes the problem much more tractable mathematically, and allows one to utilize methods already known from the theory of radiative transfer[7].

Considerable analytical ingenuity has been applied to the approximate solution of idealized problems about monoenergetic neutrons satisfying idealized scattering laws, especially in homogeneous media. Much of this research is summarized in Ref. 4, but mention should also be made of continuing work by Bellman and his co-workers, which is described by Bellman and Kalaba in Ref. 1.

§4. Multigroup diffusion equations. Most practical overall nuclear reactor computations are based on a drastic simplification of the equations of transport theory, known as multigroup diffusion theory. In the diffusion approximation, the dependent variable is taken to be the "neutron flux" $\phi(\underline{x}, v; t)$, defined as the product $vN_0(\underline{x}, v; t)$ of the neutron speed v and the average neutron density N_0 , averaged over all directions (unit vectors) $\underline{\omega}$. Mathematically,

$$N_0(\underline{x}, v; t) = \frac{1}{4\pi} \iint N(\underline{x}, v\underline{\omega}; t) dS(\underline{\omega}) \ ,$$

where dS is area on the unit sphere.

The approximations involved in passing from transport to diffusion theory have been analyzed by Marshak and others; Wilkins has ably described them in Ref. 1. In general, multigroup diffusion theory would agree exactly with neutron transport theory if the mean free path λ_t between successive collisions were negligibly short, and if the number of "velocity-groups" considered were infinitely large.

In fact, neither assumption is fulfilled too well. In water, λ_t is about 5 mm for thermal neutrons at room temperature, and may be over 2 cm for epithermal neutrons in power reactors. Whereas water channels between fuel plates may be less than 1 cm wide. The planning of realistic criticality "cell" calculations for stacks of fuel plates, spaced about one mean free neutron path apart, is a special art. (The limiting case of "infinitely close" fuel plates is much easier, being equivalent to the case of a homogeneous reactor.)

In multigroup diffusion theory, the neutrons are divided into a more or less arbitrary number n of velocity-groups. In thermal reactors, this division leads to the fundamental multigroup diffusion equations

$$(1) \quad \partial\phi_i / \partial t = v_i \left\{ \sum_k \frac{\partial}{\partial x_k}(D_i \frac{\partial\phi_i}{\partial x_k}) - \sum_i' \phi_i + \sum_{i-1} \phi_{i-1} \right\} (i = 2, \ldots, n) \ ,$$

$$(1') \quad \partial\phi_i / \partial t = v_1 \left\{ \sum_k \frac{\partial}{\partial x_k}(D_1 \frac{\partial\phi_1}{\partial x_k}) - \sum_1' \phi_1 + \nu \sum_n \phi_n \right\} \ ,$$

provided up-scattering and group-skipping are ignored (see §10).

For simplicity, many criticality calculations are based on the assumption that all neutrons, ranging in energy from over 5 Mev down to less than 0.03 ev, can be divided into two velocity groups: "fast" neutrons and " slow" neutrons, all neutrons in the same group being treated alike. That is, it is often assumed that $n = 2$ in (1)-(1'). The choices $n = 3, 4$ are also commonly used. Such crude "few-group" approximations are less inaccurate than one might think—provided the velocities v_i , diffusion coefficients $D_i = \lambda_i/3$, and cross-sections $\sum_i$, $\sum_i'$ are skillfully "averaged" [8]. This success may be related to the general mathematical tendency of the convolution of several kernels (e. g. , slowing down and thermal diffusion) to be Gaussian[9].

Some correction can be made for the finite mean free path neglected in the diffusion equations (1)-(1'), by using nominal "extrapolated boundaries" at a distance of 0.71 λ_t beyond the real boundaries of a bare reactor. This correction is based on the fit which gives the best results for monoenergetic neutrons. In the case of a core bounded by a reflector, the effect of the reflector can be approximated more generally by using an extrapolation distance $d = 0.71\lambda_t(1+\beta)/(1-\beta)$, where the "albedo factor" β depends only on the reflector[10].

But it should be stressed that, even after the simplifying approximations of few-group diffusion theory have been made, criticality calculations for heterogeneous reactor cores are very complicated. In practice, one must usually be satisfied with two-dimensional models, in which the effect of the third dimension is approximated crudely by a "buckling" parameter supposed to compensate for leakage in the transverse direction[11].

§5. Fermi age theory. Besides "two-group" and "few-group" calculations, "multigroup" calculations are often made in the diffusion approximation to neutron transport theory. The number of groups considered is never enough, however, to give a realistic picture of the resonance absorption peaks in uranium, for example. In practice, the resonance escape probability (§1) is always calculated independently.

For some reactor media, one can use an elegant analytical model involving a continuum of velocity groups, the so-called Fermi age theory in which the slowing down is treated as continuous. This model is considered to be reasonable for reactors in which the moderator is graphite, so that the average number of collisions required to slow a fission neutron down to thermal energy is over 100, instead of less than 20 (as for hydrogen).

As shown originally by Fermi and Amaldi, if the "age" τ associated with a given lethargy is defined (Ref. 2, pp. 98, 144, 176) as

$$\tau = \int_0^u \frac{\lambda_t}{3\xi\Sigma_s} du \ , \quad \text{where} \quad 3\xi \approx \frac{2}{3A+2} \ (A = \text{atomic mass}) \ ,$$

and if the "slowing down density" q is defined as $\xi\Sigma_s\phi$, then continuous slowing down should be governed by the heat conduction equation, $\partial q/\partial\tau = \nabla^2 q$, in a medium in which absorption can be neglected.

The original derivation was based on a good physical intuition as to the limiting asymptotic behavior in a medium in which all nuclei have large atomic mass A . I am glad to report that one of my students, Mr. Martin Leibowitz, has recently been able to parallel this physical reasoning, in the case of a homogeneous reactor, by a rigorous mathematical analysis of transport theory as a stochastic process.

III. SPECTRAL THEORY

§6. One-group model. Many interesting technical mathematical problems arise, when one attempts to deduce the theory of criticality from the differential and integrodifferential equations mentioned above. As I have described these problems in Reference 1 and another publication scheduled to appear fairly soon[12], I shall touch on them only briefly here. Though not particularly suitable for numerical analysis, they strike me as very suitable for abstract analysts specializing in the spectral theory of linear operators.

The best known mathematical discussions of criticality assume
expansibility in eigenfunctions (Ref. 2, pp. 357-61; Ref. 3, pp. 406
-10; Ref. 4, pp. 30-33, 195-8). One need hardly argue here that this
is a strong assumption: operator spectra need not be discrete, nor
need operators be similar to diagonal operators. Hence it is worth
mentioning that one can probably justify the possibility—always attractive to physicists—of expanding an "arbitrary" initial fission
density distribution $\phi_f(\underline{x};0)$ into orthogonal spatial eigenfunctions
with real eigenvalues, in the case of idealized bounded reactors in
the one-group approximation. This is because, if slowing down is
neglected, all neutron paths are statistically reversible.

This physical principle can be given various mathematical formulations. If one describes each neutron life-history in terms of the
position $\underline{x}_n$, velocity $\underline{u}_n$, and time t_n of its n-th collision, and
if N denotes the number of collisions from its birth at $\underline{x}_0$, then
the transformation

(2) $(\underline{x}_n, \underline{u}_n, t_n) \rightarrow (\underline{x}_{N-n}, -\underline{u}_{N-n}, t_N - t_{N-n})$

preserves scattering probabilities.

As a result, the fission-to-fission migration kernel $K(\underline{x},\underline{y};t)$,
expressing the probability density that a neutron produced by fission
at $\underline{y}$ will cause fission at $\underline{x}$ after a lifetime of t seconds, is
symmetric in the one-group approximation:

(3) $K(\underline{x},\underline{y};t) = K(\underline{y},\underline{x};t)$.

Though the kernel is singular on the diagonal, it can be smoothed by
iteration; hence it seems reasonable to expect the existence of a basis of spatial eigenfunctions $\psi_n(\underline{x})$, with associated real eigenvalues λ_n, such that the functions $\phi_f = \psi_n(\underline{x})e^{\lambda_n t}$ are solutions of
the integral equation

(4) $\phi_f(\underline{x},t) = \int_0^\infty K(\underline{x},\underline{y};\tau)\phi_f(\underline{y},t-\tau)d\tau$.

A rigorous mathematical treatment of these plausible ideas would
seem to me worthwhile, even though the one-group approximation
gives a very inaccurate description of real neutron migration.

§7. Multiplicative processes. Recently, it has become apparent
that the key to the mathematics of criticality is provided by the spectral theory of nonnegative linear operators, via the concept of a "multiplicative process". This central concept may be defined as follows:

DEFINITION. A multiplicative process is a one-parameter semi-
group of nonnegative linear operators.

It is especially natural, in a symposium on numerical analysis,
to consider first the finite-dimensional case, as only this case can
be treated in computing machines with finite storage. In this case,
nonnegative linear operators can be represented as nonnegative

matrices. Accordingly, one has <u>discrete</u> multiplicative processes, defined by nonnegative matrices P through the formula

(5) $$\underline{\phi}^{(r+1)} = \underline{\phi}^{(r)}P = \underline{\phi}^{(0)}P^{r+1} .$$

One also has <u>continuous</u> multiplicative processes, defined by "essentially" nonnegative matrices Q through the matrix differential equation

(6) $$d\underline{\phi}/dt = \underline{\phi}Q , \quad \text{or} \quad \underline{\phi}(t) = \underline{\phi}(0)e^{Qt} .$$

Here we multiply on the right, letting $\underline{\phi} = (\phi_1, \ldots, \phi_m)$ be a row m-vector; we require P to have nonnegative (real) entries, and Q to have nonnegative off-diagonal entries, which makes $e^{Qt} = I + tQ + t^2Q^2/2! + \ldots$ be nonnegative.

Markoff chains define a familiar special type of multiplicative process, in which $\underline{\phi}$ represents the expected number (precisely, mathematical <u>expectation</u>) of particles in each of m "cells" or "states". For Markoff chains, p_{ij} in (5) denotes the probability of transition from the i-th cell to the j-th cell, while q_{ij} denotes the probability per unit time of this transition in (6). For Markoff chains, $\sum_{j=1}^{m} p_{ij} = 1$ and $\sum_{j=1}^{m} q_{ij} = 0$, since particles cannot be "born" or "die"; they can only diffuse from cell to cell.

Thus, in the first instance, "multiplicative processes" can be regarded as <u>generalized Markoff processes</u>, in which birth (e.g., through nuclear fission) and death (e.g., by escape or absorption) are possible events.

§8. <u>Persistent distribution</u>; <u>importance vector</u>.

The following formulas, valid asymptotically for large r and t , are basic to the general theory of multiplicative processes:

(7) $$\underline{\phi}^{(r)} \sim Ak^r \underline{\phi}_p , \quad A = (\underline{\phi}^{(0)}, \underline{F}_p) ,$$

and

(8) $$\underline{\phi}(t) \sim Be^{Mt}\underline{\phi}_q , \quad B = (\underline{\phi}(0), \underline{F}_q) .$$

In (7), it is understood that k is a positive constant determined by P (the "multiplication factor"), while $\underline{\phi}_p$ (the "persistent distribution") and $\underline{F}_p$ (the "importance vector") are nonnegative vectors determined by P . From (7), it is evident that k must be the largest eigenvalue of P (hence also the "spectral radius"); that $\underline{\phi}_p$ is the associated eigenvector; and that $\underline{F}_p$ must be the dual eigenvector associated with the nonnegative transpose P' of P .

Conditions for the existence and uniqueness of such nonnegative eigenvectors $\underline{\phi}_p$ and $\underline{F}_p$, with eigenvalue k , can be deduced from the general theory of nonnegative matrices invented by Perron and Frobenius. Sufficient conditions have been obtained in Ref. 5, where the case of continuous processes (6), (8) is also treated, with special reference to technical problems of nuclear reactor theory.

In unpublished work, R. S. Varga and the author have further refined these results so as to obtain necessary <u>and</u> sufficient conditions for the validity of (7) and (8). A sample result is the following[13].

THEOREM 1. For a discrete multiplicative process (5) to satisfy (7) with strictly positive $\underline{\phi}_p$ and $\underline{F}_p$, it is necessary and sufficient that P be primitive. For a continuous multiplicative process (6) to satisfy (8) with strictly positive $\underline{\phi}_q$ and $\underline{F}_q$, it is necessary and sufficient that Q be irreducible.

Explanation. We will call a vector "strictly" positive, if and only if all its components are positive. An $m \times m$ nonnegative matrix P is primitive, if and only if P^m has all positive entries. An $m \times m$ essentially nonnegative matrix Q is irreducible if and only if, given $i \neq j$, one can find $k(0) = i, k(1), \cdots, k(n) = j$ such that $q_{k(s-1), k(s)}$ is non-zero for $s = 1, \cdots, n$.

In the study of <u>reactor criticality</u>, one of the most important problems is the effective numerical calculation of k and $\underline{\phi}_p$, resp. of M and $\underline{\phi}_q$, for given P and Q . The study of the best way of calculating these is certainly a very important problem in numerical analysis. But it can hardly be solved uniformly in the context of the theory of multiplicative processes in general. To appreciate the practical problem, one must keep in mind some of the characteristic physical features of nuclear reactor theory mentioned in Part I.

§9. <u>Multigroup model.</u> The significance of positive operators for reactor theory is easily explained. When slowing-down is considered, the fission-to-fission migration kernel can no longer be expected to be spatially symmetric[14]. Though the Fredholm theory of integral equations may be applicable, it seems doubtful whether it is adequate by itself to yield rigorous theorems about the existence of a critical distribution, importance function, multiplication factor k , or e-folding time $(k-1)/\ell^*$. For example, it does not imply that the "dominant" eigenvalue λ_1 with largest real part is real <u>or</u> simple. The key to these facts seems to be provided by <u>positivity</u> properties: the fact that $K(\underline{x}, \underline{y};t)$ is typically positive for $\underline{x}, \underline{y}$ in the region containing fissionable material.

The precise relation of the migration kernel to the multigroup diffusion equations (1)-(1') is still far from clear; an extension of the ideas of §§7-8 to the latter context has been made by Drs. Habetler and Martino, and reported in Ref. 1. These authors observe that each individual (self-adjoint) elliptic partial differential equation of (1)-(1') has a positive (symmetric) Green's function. These functions constitute a cycle of non-permutable integral kernels, whose cumulative effect is equivalent to that of a single <u>positive</u> and non-symmetric kernel like $\int_0^\infty K(\underline{x}, \underline{y};t)dt = K(\underline{x}, \underline{y})$. To this kernel, they apply the Theorem of Jentzsch, which is just the extension to integral equations of the

Perron-Frobenius theory of nonnegative matrices, in a generalized
form due to Krein and Rutman. The validity of (7) for unique choices
of positive k , $\underline{\phi}_p$ and $\underline{F}_p$ then follows.

It would seem to me desirable to extend these results in various
directions, such as to continuous slowing down models.

Transport model. To develop a general theory of criticality in
the transport approximation of §3 is more difficult. It has been shown
by Lehner and Wing[15] that the transport operator for slab problems
does not have a complete family of eigenfunctions. However, one
can exploit positivity concepts effectively. As I am currently doing
this myself, I shall say no more about this problem here[16].

IV. PROBLEMS OF NUMERICAL ANALYSIS

§10. General remarks. The needs for astute numerical analysis
in nuclear reactor theory, even in reactor statics, are extremely varied
and complex. The most obvious short-range problems of numerical analysis arise in connection with the multigroup diffusion equations (1)-
(1'); moreover the most important contributions by mathematicians to
nuclear reactor theory have concerned these equations; hence I shall
concentrate my attention on them below[17].

In general, the first and most important problem is to calculate
k for a system (1)-(1') and, when $k = 1$, to determine approximately
the (persistent) critical distribution whose existence is guaranteed
by the Theorem of Habetler and Martino.

In actual reactor design calculations, one assumes $k = 1$, for
the reason stated in §2: to provide stable power, k must be kept in
the range $.995 < k < 1.005$. Hence, one sets $k = 1$, which amounts
to assuming $\phi P = \phi$ in (5) and (7), and $\phi Q = 0$ $(M = 0)$ in (6) and
(8). Correspondingly, it amounts to replacing (1)-(1') by

(9) $$-\sum_k \frac{\partial}{\partial x_k}\left(D_i \frac{\partial \phi_i}{\partial x_k}\right) + \sum_i' \phi_i = \sum_{i-1} \phi_{i-1} \ (i = 2, \dots, n) \ ,$$

(9') $$-\sum_k \frac{\partial}{\partial x_k}\left(D_1 \frac{\partial \phi_1}{\partial x_k}\right) + \sum_1' \phi_1 = \nu \sum_n \phi_n \ .$$

These equations define the main problem of reactor statics: that of
finding a nonnegative stable or time-independent critical distribution.
(Some problems of reactor dynamics will be mentioned in Part V.)

Obviously, (9)-(9') have a non-trivial solution if and only if ν
is an eigenvalue of the system—and this solution is the desired one
if ν is the dominant eigenvalue. Hence, in practice one usually
bases calculations on the following formulation of the conditions for
criticality (i.e., of static equilibrium): what hypothetical average
neutron yield per fission ν_h is required to make a given reactor critical? If the hypothetical ν_h exceeds the actual ν for U^{235} , then
the reactor is subcritical; if $\nu_h < \nu$, it is supercritical; in either
case, one tries to approach the desired condition $\nu_h = \nu$ by a design

modification or fuel enrichment.

In other words, one defines ν_h as the dominant eigenvalue and computes it. If $\nu_h < \nu$, one tries to increase the reactivity; if $\nu_h > \nu$, one tries to decrease it.

In computing ν_h , one considers the spatial distributions $\underline{\phi}_k$ of neutron flux in n velocity intervals ("lethargy groups"), the components of the vectors $\underline{\phi}_1, \ldots, \underline{\phi}_n$ refer to the flux intensities in these groups at some specified grid of mesh-points. In the equation $\underline{\phi}Q = \underline{0}$, one can equate the rate $\underline{\phi}_{k-1}B_k$ at which neutron flux in the k-th lethargy group is created by the slowing down[18] (through collision) of a neutron in the (k-1)-st lethargy group, to the net rate of loss of neutron flux in the k-th lethargy group, at each mesh-point, by diffusion (i.e., scattering). This leads to a set of equations of the form

(10) $\quad \underline{\phi}_k A_k = \underline{\phi}_{k-1}B_k \qquad\qquad\qquad (k = 2, \ldots, n)$,

(10') $\quad \underline{\phi}_1 A_1 = \nu_h \underline{\phi}_n B_1 \qquad\qquad\qquad (\nu_h > 0)$.

In these equations, the matrices A_k and B_k are the usual 5-point difference approximations to (9)-(9'). The cross-sections $\sum_i$, $\sum_i'$ and diffusion coefficients D_i are deduced, in turn, from experimental data and the elastic scattering laws mentioned in §1, by complicated methods into which mathematicians should not inquire too deeply! Suffice it to say (Ref. 7) that the A_k^{-1} and B_k are nonnegative, and the B_k diagonal. Moreover the A_k are <u>symmetric</u>, since each elliptic differential equation of (9)-(9') is self-adjoint.

One can combine (10)-(10') into a single equation

(11) $\quad \underline{\phi}_n \doteq \nu_h P \underline{\phi}_n$, $P = B_1 A_1^{-1} \ldots B_n A_n^{-1}$,

where P is nonnegative. The condition for criticality, then, is that the choice $\nu_h = \nu$ should make the multiplicative process defined by (11) exactly critical. The matrix P in (11) also has an important physical interpretation, as an approximation to the <u>migration kernel</u> $K(\underline{x}, \underline{y})$ describing the probability that a neutron created by fission at $\underline{x}$ will cause fission at $\underline{y}$.

§11. <u>Inner and outer iterations</u>. Each individual equation (10) is solved in practice by a semi-iterative process referred to as "inner iteration". Clearly, each <u>inner iteration</u> can be considered as solving a <u>source problem</u>. For example, in a homogeneous reactor, the problem is to solve a modified Helmholtz equation $-\nabla^2 \phi + k^2 \phi = S(\underline{x})$ with source term. Thus it is a straightforward generalization of the problem of solving the Poisson equation $-\nabla^2 \phi = S(x)$, one of the oldest problems of numerical analysis.

Given a technique for solving such source problems, one can solve the successive individual equations in (1) and (1') in the cyclic order $i = 1, 2, \cdots, n; 1, 2, \cdots, n; \cdots$. This is called the process of "outer iteration". The considerations of positivity mentioned above, in Part III, guarantee the convergence under outer iteration to the "critical" fission distribution, of the exact solutions of the source problems mentioned in the preceding paragraph. The metric methods introduced in Ref. 6 even permit one to solve the geometric convergence of approximate solutions of these source problems to the critical distribution, provided the initial "trial distribution" ϕ_1 is positive.

Truncation error. Approximate solutions of the multigroup diffusion equations are, naturally, obtained on high-speed digital computing machines for suitable difference approximations to (1)-(1'). The accuracy of such difference approximations is analyzed in Ref. 7, with especial reference to the order of accuracy across surfaces of discontinuity, such as occur in heterogeneous reactors. However, it should be stressed that this important work by Varga by no means covers all the truncation errors arising in multigroup criticality calculations. Many unsolved problems remain for the numerical analyst.

First, there is the classical problem of replacing asymptotic order-of-magnitude truncation error estimates by realistic truncation error bounds. In spite of important recent contributions to this problem[19], it remains basically unsolved, even for the Poisson equation.

Second, there is the problem of estimating the error which is involved in replacing (one-group) transport equations by the approximation of continuous diffusion. The qualitative analysis by Wilkins in Ref. 1 will be helpful to the researcher wishing to work on this problem.

Third, it should be recalled that multigroup equations are actually discrete approximations to a continuous velocity spectrum. Hence there is also a truncation error in the lethargy which deserves study[20]. Finally, someone should analyze the truncation errors involved in synthesizing three-dimensional reactors from two-dimensional models (cf. §4).

§12. SOR methods. The problems just mentioned are extremely difficult, and it may require profound originality to make substantial progress on them. More promising in the short run, in my opinion, is the problem of improving iterative methods for solving the accepted difference approximations to the multigroup diffusion equations. Especially attractive for the novice, is the analysis of source problems. These involve sparse, symmetric, nonnegative or positive matrices, which are amenable to a great variety of mathematical techniques.

In general, the Young-Frankel technique of Systematic Overrelaxation (SOR for short) has proved to be the most successful method for solving the source problems of reactor theory. Many ingenious modifications of it have been proposed, some of which can be identified by such current phrases as "line overrelaxation", "block overrelaxation", "p-cyclic matrices" and so on. A unified discussion of these modifications has just been presented in Ref. 8, which all interested numerical analysts should read[21]. A problem of importance is the selection of "optimum overrelaxation factors" for source problems in heterogeneous reactors.

Outer iterations. The theory of outer iteration is far less developed. Assuming the near-reality of eigenvalues, one can accelerate the convergence of outer iterations by "Chebyshev polynomial" techniques described in Ref. 7. There has also been some quasi-theoretical work by Varga on the "optimum strategy" of combining inner with outer iterations. But there seems considerable room for the invention and justification of improved methods for accelerating the convergence of combined inner and outer iteration. I therefore recommend this problem to your attention, as having great theoretical and practical interest.

§13. IAD methods. Especially for "cell" calculations whose inner iterations converge slowly, the evidence so far accumulated indicates that SOR methods may become superseded by "implicit alternating direction methods" (IAD methods for short), developed by Peaceman, Rachford and Douglas[22]. However, this evidence is almost entirely experimental. Whereas Young[23] and others have given rigorous and realistic analyses of the efficiency of SOR methods, as applied to general linear self-adjoint elliptic difference equations, there exists no corresponding justification for the observed efficiency of IAD methods. The case of the Helmholtz equation in a rectangle or box (product of intervals) is the only one in which IAD methods have been justified (Ref. 9).

The development of a rigorous and realistic general analysis of the convergence of IAD methods is certainly a major problem of numerical analysis, and a very challenging one. Young, Varga and I have devoted much thought to it, and our hats will be off to anyone who improves on our results[24].

The present state of ignorance can be indicated in a few sentences. For the Helmholtz equation in a rectangle (a "box-shaped homogeneous reactor"), it is known that most rapid convergence is obtainable by using a geometric sequence of positive "iteration parameters" $\rho_1, \rho_2, \rho_3, \cdots$ sprinkled densely on some interval $a \leq \rho \leq b$. It is also known that, in this case, one can match the efficiency of SOR methods up to a factor of 2 or so by the choice of a single fixed eigenvalue suppressor ρ . But it is not known, in general, that one will obtain convergence at all, using even two such iteration parameters in alternation: $\rho_1, \rho_2, \rho_1, \rho_2, \rho_1, \cdots$.

§14. Transport calculations. Another field which is in need of rigorous numerical analysis is that of transport calculations. Many one-dimensional transport equations of the Boltzmann type (§3) have been solved numerically, and by various methods. Several of these methods have been reviewed in Ref. 4. One of the most practical for reactor calculations is Carlson's S_n method, reviewed by Carlson in Ref. 1. Others are the so-called P_n or "spherical harmonic" approximation; the closely related method of "discrete ordinates"; the double P_n method; and the method of "invariant embedding" (see the end of §3).

Like the multigroup diffusion equations, the transport equations can only be solved approximately by iterative methods. Therefore, they pose to the numerical analyst the two problems of speeding up convergence and minimizing the truncation error. In spite of the vast literature on radiation transfer, only a few published papers contain technical numerical analyses of either problem.

Since the equations of transport theory describe multiplicative processes, it is pretty clear from Perron-Frobenius theory that suitable discretizations of transport equations must be solvable by convergent iterative processes. Some applications of this idea have been published by Bareiss, and by Gelbard, Davis, and Pearson[25].

The convergence to zero of the truncation errors of the P_n and discrete ordinate approximations, as $n \to \infty$, has been proved by Krook and Anselone[26] for one-dimensional transport models. But the coefficients $c_k(x)$ of the Legendre expansion $J(x, \mu) = \Sigma\, c_k(x) P_k(\mu)$, and the related functions $J(x, \mu_k) = a_k(x)$ of the discrete ordinate method are treated by both authors as functions of a continuous variable x . It would be desirable to extend their results to the case of discrete x . Thus, the study of convergence rates and truncation errors for two-dimensional, completely discrete transport problems offers many rich research opportunities.

From a more immediate practical standpoint, the development of effective digital methods for solving two-dimensional transport problems, thus reducing the truncation error of multigroup calculations, would seem to me to be very important. Carlson is now extending his S_n method so as to be applicable to such problems, but there is obviously room for competition!

Monte Carlo methods. No discussion of reactor calculations would be complete without some mention of the efficacy of Monte Carlo sampling methods, developed by S. Ulam during World War II, with reactor applications in mind. For example, these can be used to estimate prompt neutron lifetimes ℓ^* and resonance escape probabilities from two-dimensional transport equations, with considerable accuracy. In this sense, they provide a partial solution to the practical problem just stated; the techniques involved are described by Richtmyer in Ref. 1. However, they do not solve the practical problem completely, because they do not yet provide an efficient means for calculating spatial distributions with satisfactory local detail[27].

Equally basic, it seems to me, is the need for a rigorous analysis of the statistical errors of Monte Carlo methods, resting on such secure foundations as the Law of Large Numbers and the Central Limit Theorem. An important step in this direction has been made by J. Spanier[28], who has applied probability theory to various general concepts such as importance sampling and expected value sampling. But we are still far from the desirable state of knowing in advance, with any accuracy, how many sample neutron life histories will have to be followed through in a given problem before the results will be accurate with a probable error of (say) 0.3%. Hence there remains much technical work to be done by the numerical analyst in this area, too.

V. REACTOR DYNAMICS

§15. Reactor kinetics. As already stated, one must keep the multiplication factor k very near one in power reactors. Therefore, the first problem of reactor kinetics is to estimate the effect on k of minor perturbations, changing k by less than 0.5%. Evidently, an attempt to estimate such perturbation effects from a straightforward comparison of numerical results introduces delicate considerations of numerical analysis, concerning which little has been published[29]. (In practice, differences in k as small as 0.1% have been reliably inferred from static criticality calculations, by direct numerical comparison. The validity of such comparison has been justified by Dr. A. F. Henry in unpublished work.)

A serious study of this problem must take into account the phenomenon of delayed neutrons, already mentioned in §2. This is usually done by the so-called one-region reactor kinetic equations (Ref. 2. p. 295)

$$(12) \qquad \partial\phi/\partial t = \frac{1}{\ell} \{[(1 - \beta)k - 1]\phi + \sum_{i=1}^{5} \lambda_i C_i\}$$

$$(12') \qquad \partial C_i/\partial t = -\lambda_i C_i + (k \sum_a)\beta_i \phi \ , \quad i = 1, \ldots, 5 \ .$$

The integration of this system of ordinary differential equations provides a challenge to the numerical analyst, because its coefficients vary by orders of magnitude, from $1/\ell \simeq 10^4 \ \mathrm{sec}^{-1}$ to $\lambda_5 \simeq 0.02$ sec^{-1} . Also, the coefficients β_i are very small!

In practice, (12)-(12') serve primarily as a definition of k(t) ; the effective calculation of k(t) from observations of $\phi(t)$ requires considerable analytical ingenuity[30]. It would be very desirable to have available difference methods for integrating (12)-(12') numerically in a reasonable amount of time as well. Such a procedure would constitute a first step towards a realistic numerical treatment of reactor kinetics on the basis of a matrix differential equation of the form (6).

It would also be a first step towards a systematic analysis of multiregion reactor kinetics, an important subject which has so far been treated only by very approximate analytical methods in a few special cases[31]. Evidently, the "one-region" reactor kinetic equations (12)-(12') are based on taking spatial flux "averages" in a sense which has never been precisely defined. They are incapable of predicting spatial flux oscillations; moreover the "prompt neutron lifetime" ℓ is derived from experimental data indirectly. Clearly, one would like to be able to predict when spatial flux oscillations are likely to occur, and also when to expect variations in the prompt neutron lifetime!

§16. Reactor dynamics. I believe that numerical analysts should be able to make important contributions to the problems just mentioned. However, it should be emphasized that reactor kinetic calculations represent only a small part of the much larger and more difficult problem of reactor dynamics.

In the discussion of Part III, it was assumed that the matrices P
and Q defining the multiplicative processes (5) and (6) were time-
independent; unless one makes this assumption, it is difficult to define
"criticality" precisely[32]. In fact, reactor criticality is time-dependent.

It is evident that this must be so on a sufficiently long time-scale.
By definition, an efficient power reactor must "burn up" a sizeable
fraction of its fuel, changing the reactor characteristics by lowering
its criticality. (In engineering practice, this must be compensated for
by control rod withdrawal or by the use of "burnable poisons".) Fuel
depletion calculations can be made, in principle, by simulating the
actual critical fission distribution, and changing such macroscopic
cross-sections as $\Sigma_f(\underline{x})$ progressively, to allow for the integrated
power[33]. In practice, such calculations are very slow and expensive.

To be realistic, they must take into account "fission product
poisoning", an important phenomenon ignored in §§1-2, and not anticipated by early nuclear physicists. Such intermediate fission products
as Xe^{135} and Sm^{149} are neutron absorbing "poisons", which have a
half-life of hours (Ref. 2, pp. 329-39). These products have an important delayed effect on the reactivity, which is analogous to (but
opposite in direction, and on a longer time scale) that of delayed neutrons. Hence, it can be estimated by methods analogous to those used
in reactor kinetics.

More interesting mathematically is the analysis of short-term reactor stability. Here one usually assumes that the power-to-reactivity
feedback operator is linear. The coupled system formed by (12)-(12')
and this operator define a nonlinear dynamical system for any reactor;
the stability of systems of this type have been the subject of various
interesting mathematical investigations[34].

§17. Temperature coefficients; conclusion. Much more trouble-
some, partly because it occurs on a short time-scale (e.g., of seconds) is the estimation of so-called reactivity temperature coefficients
(Ref. 2, pp. 339-44). Temperature variations in a power reactor appreciably change its multiplication factor in at least three ways. First,
by increasing the mean velocity of absorbing nuclei, the resonance
absorption bands undergo a "Doppler broadening" with decreased intensity when a reactor becomes hot. The total area $\int \Sigma_a(v)dv$ under
the curve is unchanged, but there is a resulting net decrease in reactivity, especially for lumped absorbers such as control rods. The problem of estimating the net effect a priori involves all the complications
of resonance escape calculations, and so it should be left to profes-
sional physicists.

Second, the change in equilibrium velocity of the thermal neutrons with
temperature alters the cross-sections for thermal neutrons, and hence (for
example) the ratio of those which leak out to those which cause fission.

Finally, and often most important, heating causes thermal expansion and decreased density, especially in boiling reactors. This effect is apt to be very difficult to calculate, and is probably best left
to experts in real fluid mechanics and heat transfer. —Furthermore,
in reactor power plants, the reactor dynamics involve flow rates in

secondary loops, external power demand, and many other factors[35].
Hence I would leave them to the practical power plant engineer!

The mathematician's best introduction to nuclear reactor problems
is surely through the analysis of reactor statics. If I have mentioned
other problems, it has been primarily to round out the picture, and to
convince you that there are enough important problems in nuclear reactor theory to keep many numerical analysts busy for many years. If I
have one final thought to leave with you, it is that serious progress on any
one of the problems I have mentioned is likely to require months or even
years of work, while fundamental progress will require real inspiration!

FOOTNOTES

1. The accuracy of these remarks has been substantially improved
by friendly criticisms of H. L. Garabedian, A. F. Henry, J. J. Taylor,
and R. S. Varga.

2. For cross-section data, see D.J. Hughes and R. B. Schwartz,
"Neutron cross-sections", U. S. Govt., 1958.

3. It ignores the phenomena of neutron diffraction ("coherent scattering"), which is unimportant. And it must be modified to take account of molecular binding, which is very important.

4. Or "branching process", in the terminology of T. E. Harris, Persons interested in the mathematical foundations of the subject should
consult Harris' forthcoming book on "Branching processes", Springer,
1960.

5. See Ref. 3, Ch. IX, for an excellent discussion. For a scholarly
review of the literature, see also Ref. 4.

6. Some two-dimensional calculations for idealized monoenergetic
neutrons are reported in K. Case, F. de Hoffman and G. Placzek,
"Introduction to the theory of neutron diffusion", Los Alamos, 1953.

7. See E. Hopf, "Mathematical problems of radiative equilibrium",
Cambridge Tract No. 31, 1934; S. Chandrasekhar, "Radiative transfer", Oxford, 1950; V. Kourganoff and I. W. Busbridge, "Basic methods in transfer problems", Oxford, 1952.

8. See the articles by R. Ehrlich and M. S. Nelkin in Ref. 1.

9. See Ref. 2, p. 369. With some moderators, the "slowing down
length"is also relatively small (Ref. 2, pp. 127, 183), compared with
the "diffusion length". This also tends to make a subdivision into
many velocity-groups unnecessary.

10. Ref. 2, pp. 129-36. For a theoretical discussion, applicable to
the one-group diffusion approximation, see G. Birkhoff, "Reflector
functions for elliptic equations", Proc. Symposium on Boundary Problems in Differential Equations, ed. Rudolph E. Langer, Univ. of
Wisconsin Press, Madison, 1959.

11. See for example J. E. Meyer, Report WAPD-T-723.

12. G. Birkhoff, "Lattices in applied mathematics", Proc. Symposium on Lattice Theory, to be published by the Am. Math. Soc. See also S. Karlin, J. math. mech. 8 (1959), 907-38.

13. The proof is a straightforward application of the ideas of Ref. 5, using matrix techniques treated in F. R. Gantmacher, "Theory of matrices", 2 vols., Chelsea, 1959.

14. If it were, the persistent distribution and importance function of any reactor would be the same!

15. See the article by M. Wing in Ref. 1; also G. H. Pimbley, J. math. mech. 8 (1959), 837-66.

16. Some preliminary results were announced in the Proc. Nat. Acad. Sci. 45 (1959), 567-9; I have also discussed the ideas involved in Ref. 1.

17. I shall say little about _variational methods_. For computational applications of such methods, in the multigroup approximation, see R. T. Ackroyd. The transport theory approximation is treated in the Harvard Doctoral Thesis of G. Calame, 1959.

18. This simplified discussion ignores many phenomena which can occur in many-group models. Among these may be mentioned "epithermal fission", or contributions to the right side of (9') from $\phi_1, \ldots, \phi_{n-1}$; "up-scattering" from ϕ_n to ϕ_{n-1} due to collisions with moving nuclei; and "group-skipping" in hydrogeneous media, whereby (9) should include terms in $\Sigma_{i-2}\phi_{i-2}$, etc.

19. J. L. Walsh and D. Young, J. math. phys. MIT 36 (1957), 138-50; P. Laasonen, J. ass. comp. mach. 5 (1958), 32-8. Other refs. are given in these papers.

20. As already remarked, the nature of this contribution to the truncation error is extremely complex, because of resonance bands.

21. Attention should be called also to the the unpublished Ph. D. Thesis of W. Kahan, "Gauss-Seidel methods for solving large systems of linear equations", University of Toronto, 1959.

22. D. W. Peaceman and H. H. Rachford, Jr., J. soc. ind. appl. math. 3 (1955), 28-41; J. Douglas, Jr., and H. H. Rachford, Jr., Trans. Am. Math. Soc. 82 (1956), 421-39.

23. D. Young, Trans. Am. Math. Soc. 76 (1954), 92-11. It is not always recognized that this general rigorous justification was the major contribution of Young's doctoral thesis (1950).

24. We plan to incorporate them in a review article next year. Attention should be drawn also to R. S. Varga, Report WAPD-T-1019, and to a forthcoming article in J. soc. ind. app. math. by G. Habetler and E. Wachspress, dealing with the same subject.

25. E. H. Bareiss, David Taylor Model Basin Report 1030 (1956); E. Belbard, J. Davis and J. Pearson, Nuclear sci. eng. 5 (1959), 36-44 and 6 (1959), 251-2. The results of Bareiss have been extended in unpublished work by John Bennett.

26. P. M. Anselone, Astrophys. J. 128 (1958), 124-9 and J. math. mech. 7 (1958), 557-70; M. Krook, Astrophys. J. 122 (1955), 488-97, 129 (1959), 724-33, and 130 (1959), 286-95.

27. The adaptation of Monte Carlo methods to the estimation of detailed spatial distributions, by "smoothing" or other techniques, is another major problem for the ambitious numerical analyst.

28. Report WAPD-195, Westinghouse Atomic Power Div., Bettis Plant.

29. The only reference known to me is S. Margolis and S. Kaplan, Report WAPD-T-1067.

30. See for example H. C. Corben, Nuclear sci. eng. 5 (1959), 127-31. An excellent general study of reactor kinetics is contained in Soodak's article in Ref. 1.

31. H. L. Garabedian and C. B. Leffert, Nuclear Sci. Eng. 6 (1959), 26-32. See also A. F. Henry and N. J. Curlee, Nuclear sci. eng. 3 (1958), 52-70.

32. See A. F. Henry, Nuclear sci. eng. 3 (1958), 52-70.

33. See for example G. W. Hoffman, WAPD-TM-2, Westinghouse Atomic Power Division, Bettis Plant.

34. See Welton and Ergen in Ref. 1; also J. A. Nohel, MRC Tech. Summary Report No. 69, January, 1959, and unpublished papers by Nohel and J. J. Levin. See also H. P. Smets and E. P. Gyftopoulos, Nuclear sci. eng. 6 (1959), 341-9.

35. See H. Brooks, in Ref. 1; M. A. Schultz, "Control of nuclear reactors and power plants", McGraw-Hill, 1955.

REFERENCES

[1] "Proceedings of a Symposium on Nuclear Reactor Theory", to be published by the American Mathematical Society (1960?).

[2] S. Glasstone and M. C. Edlund, "The elements of nuclear reactor theory", van Nostrand, 1952.

[3] A. M. Weinberg and E. P. Wigner, "The physical theory of neutron chain reactors", Univ. of Chicago Press, 1958.

[4] B. Davison, "Neutron transport theory", Oxford, 1957.

[5] G. Birkhoff and R. S. Varga, "Reactor criticality and nonnegative matrices", J. soc. ind. appl. math. 6 (1958), 354-77.

[6] G. Birkhoff, "Extensions of Jentzsch's Theorem", Trans. Am. Math. Soc. 85 (1957), 219-27.

[7] R. S. Varga, "Numerical solution of the two-group diffusion equa-
     tion in x-y geometry", Inst. Radio Eng. Trans., Pref. Group on
     Nuclear Science NS-4 (1957), 52-62.

[8] R. S. Varga, "Factorization and normalized iterative methods",
     Proc. Symposium on Boundary Problems in Differential Equations,
     Ed. by R. E. Langer, University of Wisconsin Press, Madison,
     1959.

[9] Garrett Birkhoff and R. S. Varga, "Implicit alternating direction
     methods", Trans. Am. Math. Soc. 92 (1959), 13-24.

Discussion of Paper Two

Dr. Smagorinsky: I found your remarks on this IAD method rather interesting. We had a similar problem...to solve a Poisson equation with Dirichlet boundary conditions in a cyclic strip, for which we knew certain integral properties of the solutions. In using normal systematic relaxation techniques, we had extremely slow convergence as far as the integral property being satisfied is concerned, so we did the following:

Every time we calculated the provisional solution along one row by systematic relaxation methods, we adjusted this solution pointwise such as to satisfy the known integral—that is, we distributed the error uniformly—and went on to the next row. We found this speeded up convergence by a factor of perhaps ten. However this cannot be applied indefinitely since the error of distributing the residual uniformly eventually becomes comparable to the iterative error during the process of convergence. This technique seems to be somewhat related to the IAD method you described.

Dr. Birkhoff: Did you publish your work, or are you in process of it?

Dr. Smagorinsky: It is published.

Dr. Birkhoff: Where?

Dr. Smagorinsky: It's part of a larger work which is published in the Monthly Weather Review[*]. I have a copy if you would like to see it.

Dr. Birkhoff: Good...I thought other people here would be interested in it...that's the real thing.

Dr. Smagorinsky: I don't see why this couldn't be extended to real two-dimensional domains where we do not have cyclic continuity in one of the dimensions.

Dr. Householder: With regard to this IAD method, the difficulties of analyzing that method and getting rigorous factors is essentially the same type of difficulty one runs into when getting the spectral radius of the matrix which is used for iterating in the Gauss-Seidel method, relating the spectral radius of this matrix with the spectral characteristics of the matrix that you start with. In the implicit alternating direction method you were using a slightly modified matrix, or you can look at it that you are decomposing the original matrix in two ways and you are taking the product of these two, and therefore

---

[*]Smagorinsky, J., 1958, On the numerical integration of the primitive equations of motion for baroclinic flow in a closed region, Monthly Weather Review, 86, 457-466.

you need to consider the spectral radius of this product matrix, each of these factors is a type of decomposition of the original. You can actually get some results of rigorous stability in some rather simple cases, but I would be interested myself in a reprint of this paper in which this analogous method is used.

Dr. Birkhoff: Yes, I think it's important to distinguish between having a good method and understanding the method. We are here, I think, a group of people who appreciate the importance of understanding a method, and I am not sure whether it's surprising we don't understand the IAD method or whether it's remarkable that we do understand rigorously the variants of the SOR method, but there is a tremendous difference between these on that level. Of course, the SOR method is also a Gauss-Seidel type of method, and so are its variants, but nevertheless because the matrices are symmetrizable and deal with permutable matrices, you can handle everything theoretically.

Dr. Garabedian: Although I am not a physicist, I thought I might be so bold as to venture an opinion as to why Professor Birkhoff had trouble identifying cross-sections as tabulated by the Brookhaven National Laboratory with the ones used in actual calculations of reactor physics. Do you suppose that this difficulty is related to the fact that physicists are in the habit of averaging cross-sections over a Maxwellian neutron distribution in the thermal energy group? Sometimes this procedure isn't good enough, and physicists go to great lengths in studying distortions of the Maxwellian because of changes in neutron temperature and various intrinsic properties of the medium under study.

Dr. Birkhoff: I think thermal is not as hard to understand as the fast cross-sections. Those are the ones that are difficult.

Dr. Mann: If you consider a two-dimensional problem where you have just two regions separated by an interface with an interior corner point, but otherwise keep the problem as simple as possible, say stick to one group with very simple geometry, do you have any ideas about what conditions to impose at that interior corner point either in a finite difference approximation or at some kind of analytical approximation?

Dr. Birkhoff: You are asking, what would be a transport theory correction?

Dr. Mann: Yes.

Dr. Birkhoff: This is one of the problems I posed to this graduate student...I don't know the answer. It's a good question.

Dr. Kopal: I should like to mention, in this connection, that the solution of Milne's equation in both plane and spherical coordinates on electronic computing machines has been investigated in Manchester in the past two or three years in the doctoral thesis of Dr. T. W. Olle. The material is not yet published, as its author since has left the University for the computing field (his present address is at the SHAPE Computing Center, The Hague, Holland), and I am afraid he is not a very prompt writer. If anybody should be interested in full details, however, I am sure Dr. Olle would be glad to communicate his results in advance of publication.

Paper Three | ZDENĚK KOPAL

Numerical Problems of
Contemporary Celestial Mechanics

The celestial mechanics and numerical analysis have a long line of evolution in common. This is no accident, but a consequence of two facts of historical significance. As is well known, since the days of Newton the dynamical astronomy became the first branch of modern science to be based on a natural law of far-reaching exactitude; and, secondly, the determination of the positions of celestial bodies moving in accordance with this law has gradually developed into the most precise kind of measurement attainable in any branch of physical science. A comparison of such accurate observations with the theory of motion as developed successively by a brilliant pleiad of mathematicians from Newton, Euler, Lagrange, and Gauss to Poincaré — to name only the greatest—was bound to maintain increasing demands on the development of adequate computational techniques; and this, in turn, gave largely rise to numerical analysis as a scientific discipline. In fact, until quite recently, the astronomers (together with geodesists) have been the principal protagonists of scientific computation, and responsible for the development of a large part of the techniques now in use; at least any astronomer using the formulae which carry the names of Laplace, Gauss or Bessel and many others must feel about them quite like at home.

Throughout most part of the history of celestial mechanics, the principal task of our predecessors has been to develop a theory of the apparent motion of the major bodies of our solar system which should agree with their observed positions within the limits of observational errors. This has been largely accomplished in the 19th century by the great technicians of the generation between Laplace and Leverrier; and the way in which the residual discrepancy encountered in the secular motion of Mercury's perihelion eventually turned up to give support to the general theory of relativity is too well known to warrant more than a passing notice at this time.

If these feats have rendered the celestial mechanics pre-eminent among exact sciences of the nineteenth century, its own pinnacle of prestige and difficulty, was without doubt the theory of the motion of the Moon. Beginning with Newton, this great problem continued to exercise the ingenuity of the best minds of many successive generations up to almost our own time; and the list of the recipients of prizes offered by various academies of the world for outstanding contributions to this subject—including as it does Clairaut and d'Alembert (1747), Euler (1753, 1772), Laplace (1787), Hansen (1838, 1862), Delaunay (1860, 1867), Hill (1878), Adams (1892) and Brown (1896)—represents a veritable pantheon of our science. Most of these men beginning with Hansen have dedicated to this problem the best efforts of their lifetimes; and the fact that they failed to solve it satisfactorily bespeaks fully its intrinsic difficulty.

A literal development of lunar theory at the hands of Delaunay led to analytic expansions containing several hundred periodic terms; and beyond about seven hundred of them we still find ourselves in a mathematical no-man's land where no two investigators agree as yet with each other; and, moreover, years of individual effort would be required to penetrate any further. Therefore, the recent decades have witnessed a partial retreat from analytic theories of lunar motion to purely numerical ones, which can give us accurate answers for a limited time, but without sufficient insight into the identity of all contributing forces. One can perhaps sum up the present situation by stating that no satisfactory lunar theory has emerged as yet from this cumulative effort, and the Moon—as if aware of it—still occasionally fails to run on time!

My principal aim today is not, however, to dwell on any intricacies of the motion of our natural satellite, but rather to concentrate on a new class of problems which have suddenly come to confront us in October 1957 when the first artificial satellite began to revolve around this Earth, and was soon followed by others which ventured even further afield in the inter-planetary space. Any broader discussion of their significance is wholly beyond the scope of my present remarks; for these are to be limited solely to some problems arising from the interpretation of <u>motions</u> of such satellites as can be observed from the surface of the Earth by optical methods or radio-techniques.

From the point of view of the terrestrial astronomer, an artificial satellite represents a mass point (or rigid body) moving in the given gravitational field of force in accordance with the well-known equations of motion. If this field were due solely to a simple gravitational pole located at the center of the Earth (which would be true if the Earth were a sphere), the relative orbit of our mass-particle around it would, of course, be a conic. However, if the forces acting on the satellite are more complicated, its trajectory would be bound to depart from a closed conic; and an analysis of such departures should, in turn, offer an excellent opportunity to investigate the nature of the individual components contributing to this field of force from the observed orbital perturbations.

Before we survey the nature of individual forces giving rise to such perturbations, let it be stressed that the time range of the observational material, which is already now at our disposal, compares favorably with that available for most other celestial bodies. In order to appreciate it, let us remember that the average period of revolution of the Earth satellites launched so far is about two hours (see Table 1). This corresponds to approximately 4400 revolutions per annum; and the U. S. Vanguard I satellite (1958β), which, thanks to the solar batteries included in its ten pound payload, still continues to report to the Minitrack stations on Earth, has since its launching on March 17, 1958, already completed more revolutions around the Earth than the number of years which has elapsed since the dawn of human civilization. This makes it also obvious that it would be highly impracticable to follow it in the sky by attempting to integrate the equations of motion continuously over so many cycles. Instead, we find it expedient to represent its orbit by an instantaneous ellipse (or other type of a curve) whose elements vary continuously with the time, and to integrate equations governing the variation of such elements caused by a specific perturbing function. Whether or not the basic curve subject to perturbations should be a Keplerian ellipse or another integrable approximation to the actual orbit which takes account of at least a part of the actual perturbations [1] remains yet to be seen. The former approach possesses—at least temporarily—the advantage that the exact form of the variational equation is well known—and has been so since the days of Lagrange; all we have to do is insert in them the appropriate perturbing function.

Of the principal constituents which such a function is bound to contain in any realistic approach to our problem, the following sources of perturbations must be considered.

(1) resistance offered to moving bodies by the terrestrial atmosphere (including, apart from neutral drag, the possible electromagnetic effects "induction drag" experienced if a charged satellite moves across the lines of force of the terrestrial magnetic field);

(2) perturbations arising from the rotational distortion of the terrestrial globe; and

(3) perturbations due to the attraction of the Sun and the Moon.

In order to assess the relative importance of perturbations arising from these sources, let us set out to evaluate the instantaneous accelerations exerted by these perturbing forces on typical satellites listed in the accompanying Table 1. On the surface of the Earth, at the mean distance of 6371 km from its center, the mass of the Earth is known to produce an acceleration of 981 cm/sec^2—and, at a distance r kms from the Earth's center, this acceleration should be equal to $981 \, (R_{\oplus}/r)^2$ cm/sec^2 , where $R_{\oplus}$ = 6371.22 km. It is the centrifugal force counteracting this term which is primarily responsible for main features of the satellite's orbit around the Earth.

The diurnal rotation of the Earth causes the latter to become, to a first approximation, a rotational spheroid characterized by a distortion of $-14.2 \, P_2(\nu)$ km , where ν stands for the cosine of co-latitude; and superposed on this is a small but significant fourth harmonic varying as $P_4(\nu)$. Its observational determination (from gravimetric measurements) encounter difficulties; but a quantitative theory of the equilibrium of rotating compressible fluids [2] of the structure inferred for the Earth from seismological evidence [3] reveals that the amplitude of the terrestrial fourth-harmonic distortion should be close to 32 meters—i.e., comparable with the height of the semi-diurnal tides raised on the terrestrial oceans by the combined attraction of the Sun and the Moon.

Now the terms in the disturbing gravitational potential arising from these distortions produce accelerations amounting to $-1.08 \ (R_{\oplus}/r)^4 P_2(\nu) \, cm/sec^2$ for the second-harmonic rotational distortion and $0.004 \ (R_{\oplus}/r)^6 P_4(\nu) \, cm/sec^2$ for the fourth harmonic.

It may be of interest to remark that this latter amount is already of the same order of magnitude as the gravitational effects produced by the lunar semi-diurnal tides over the Pacific and other major oceans of the terrestrial globe. In fact, there are several partial tides whose gravitational effect should produce fluctuating accelerations of the order of $0.001 \ cm/sec^2$ on artificial satellites flying above them; they are the probable cause of what Whipple [4] referred to as the "gravitational noise"; and no genuine improvement of our present knowledge of the total perturbing function can clearly be achieved until their effects have been duly accounted for. I am, of course, speaking of the dynamical tides; the equilibrium (bodily) tides of both lunar and solar origin are much too small to concern us at the present time. Their theoretical amplitudes are but 70 cm for the lunar semi-diurnal tide, and 32 cm for the solar tide—and the finite rigidity of the Earth reduces them to about 44 percent of their theoretical values [5]. The accelerations produced by such tides are then of the order of 4.5×10^{-12} and $2.1 \times 10^{-12} \, cm/sec^2$, respectively; and their effects should be utterly negligible. This is, incidentally, true also of the atmospheric tides— except, perhaps, in one respect. It is well known that the amplitudes of atmospheric semi-diurnal tides are increased greatly in excess of their equilibrium values by a near-resonance with the diurnal period of thermal insolation [6]. While the air masses displaced in this way are again much too small to produce significant gravitational perturbations, the surfaces of equal density in the upper atmosphere may indeed deviate considerably from spheres; and the atmospheric densities deduced from the observed satellite decelerations might depend on the orientation of this perigee radius vector with respect to the atmospheric tidal bulge.

Now let us compare the various gravitational accelerations quoted in the foregoing paragraphs with the radial decelerations to be expected from the atmospheric resistance. At the altitudes comprised between the perigee and apogee distances of all satellites listed in Table 1, the mean free path of atmospheric gas is already large in comparison with the dimensions of these satellites; and, in consequence, the (neutral) drag should be a resultant of the collisions between the moving body and the surrounding gas particles. If we disregard some uncertainty arising from the nature of such collisions (i.e., whether they are elastic or non-elastic), the force caused by drag should be approximately given by $\pi R^2 \, \rho v^2 g \, cm/sec^2$ [7] where πR^2

stands for the cross-section area of the satellite; v , for its speed; and ρ , for the surrounding atmospheric density. This force should, in turn, give rise to a deceleration of $\pi(R^2/m)\rho\, r^2$ cm/sec^2 , where m denotes the mass of our satellite.

If we adopt, for the sake of a comparison, $v = 8 \times 10^5$ cm/sec and $R^2/m = 10^{-2}$ cm^2/g (corresponding to $R = 10$ cm for a 20 pound satellite, or $R = 100$ cm for a 2000 pound one), deceleration due to atmospheric drag should amount to $2.0 \times 10^{10}\rho$ cm/sec^2 . Now adopting the best values available so far for air densities in the upper atmosphere [8, 9] we find that, below some 130 kms, the atmospheric drag should constitute without doubt the most important source of perturbations acting upon the carrier rocket. However, at altitudes between 130-140 km, where the prevailing density drops to 2×10^{-10}g/cm^3 , the effects of atmospheric drag should be no more than comparable in magnitude with the gravitational effects of the second-harmonic equatorial bulge of the Earth. The atmospheric density keeps, moreover, diminishing with altitude at so rapid a rate that, around 200 km above sea level (where $\rho = 4 \times 10^{-13}$g/cm^3), the atmospheric deceleration should be no greater than the gravitational effects of the fourth-harmonic rotational distortion of the Earth; and above this height—which means practically in the entire range of motions of all satellites listed in Table 1—the gravitational effects of terrestrial distortion completely predominate over atmospheric ones. This makes it obvious that no meaningful determinations of atmospheric densities can be deduced from satellite motions unless all major gravitational effects have been duly accounted for; and the fact that, in particular, the fourth-harmonic rotational distortion of the Earth (or the principal tidal effects) have so far been altogether neglected by many investigators, or given at best a rather cavalier treatment, makes one suspect whether or not the serious discrepancies in upper atmospheric densities reported to exist between the satellite and rocket determinations [8, 9, 10] are really genuine.

In enumerating the gravitational perturbations, due attention must still be paid to the attraction of the Sun and the Moon. The masses and distances of these two bodies are such that, on the surface of the Earth (and at reasonable heights aloft) their attraction will invoke velocity changes in the direction of the disturbing radius-vector amounting to 0.0054 cm/sec^2 for the Moon. These values—small as they are—turn out to be comparable with the second-order effects of polar flattening of the Earth and at least as important as (neutral) atmospheric drag even at the perigee distances of most satellites. Their neglect in reducing the observed satellite motions would, therefore, again be bound to open the way to serious systematic errors in determinations of the atmospheric densities.

Speaking of the drag, it is impossible to bypass without mentioning a most interesting discovery, by Jacchia [11], of the existence of a remarkable correlation (at least for Vanguard I and Sputnik III) between observed small fluctuations of orbital velocities of these satellites and the 27-day period of axial rotation of the Sun—

indicating that the upper-atmospheric phenomena giving rise to a drag
on the satellites respond to some aspects of solar activity. The fact
that the conspicuous solar flare of July 7, 1958, produced a notice-
able jerk in the motion of Sputnik III after a time-lag of approximately
24 hours, indicated beyond doubt that the cause of the disturbance
must have been associated with a burst of solar corpuscular radiation,
carrying a charge which was apparently sufficient to influence the motion of these satellites by appreciable amounts.

Now it is well known from the Maxwell's equation that a charged
body moving through a conducting medium in a magnetic field (provided,
in our case, by the Earth) that has a component normal to the direction
of motion, an electric current is induced in the conductor and (on account of the dissipation of energy through Joule's heat) the body experi-
ences a resistance to its motion which can be described as an
"induction drag", or "electromagnetic viscosity" according to its physical dimension. As the ionosphere and the space above it must be regarded as conducting media, electric currents must be introduced in
any metallic body (such as a satellite) moving through it, and cause it
to experience an induction drag whenever it traverses a magnetic field
in its path [7, 12, 13].

If we assume, reasonably enough, that there are some 10^6 charged
particles per ccm at height corresponding to the perigee distances of
most satellites, the intensity of the induction current in a satellite
characterized by $R = 100$ cm should be of the order of 10^{-3} amps; and
it can be shown [14] that, under these conditions, the consequent induction drag may become of the same order of magnitude as the neutral
drag arising from collisions with neutral air particles. As this latter
drag is proportional to the cross-section of the moving body, while the
induction drag is proportional to its volume, the relative importance of
the "electromagnetic viscosity" will increase with increasing dimensions of the satellite, and may become entirely dominant for large space
vehicles of the future.

Whether or not this phenomenon can explain quantitatively the observed irregularities in motion of the Vanguard I and Sputnik III insofar
as they are correlated with the solar activity remains yet to be established. A quantitative agreement would seem to require that the corpuscular radiation emitted by solar flares should charge the satellites
up to a potential of several thousand volts—a phenomenon difficult to
reconcile with the facts reported by the Russian investigators for Sputnik III. Whether or not this is exactly the case remains, of course, to
be ascertained by future experiments. However, the striking correlation which apparently exists between the perturbations in motion of
artificial satellites and specific solar phenomena leaves but little room
for doubt that, in full generality, the problem of resistance experienced
by artificial satellites in their motion around the Earth is one of hydromagnetics as much as of the kinetic theory of neutral gases.

How should this situation change with increasing distance of the
satellite from the Earth? A glance at the relevant perturbation terms reveals that they vary with relatively high inverse powers of r and, as

a result, with increasing distance from the Earth their magnitude will
rapidly drop to insignificance. For $r > 2R_\oplus$, all atmospheric resistance (whether due to the neutral or charged particles) becomes effectively nil, so that only the gravitational terms need henceforth to be
considered in the perturbing function. As we have pointed out before,
the most important of these is due to the second-harmonic rotational
distortion of the terrestrial globe: and the amplitude of the acceleration produced by it at $r = 10\, R_\oplus$ reduces to one ten-thousandth of its
surface value of 1.08 cm/sec^2 , or to about 10^{-4}cm/sec^2—which is
well-nigh negligible in comparison with the perturbations produced by
the Sun or the Moon. Therefore, beyond a distance of (say) 10 $R_\oplus$
from the Earth, any mass-particle moves freely under the gravitational
influence of the Sun, the Moon and the Earth—all of which can be regarded as mass-points.

   These perturbations are, in general, much smaller than those
which an artificial satellite or lunar probe has experienced in the more
immediate neighborhood of the Earth. Nevertheless, as they act over
longer periods of time, their cumulative effects can become so large
as to require quite accurate treatment.

   The perturbations due to the Sun vary but slightly in magnitude
as well as direction in the space between the Earth and the Moon. In
their analytic treatment, we have no justification to expect that the
eccentricity of the particle orbit, or its inclination to the ecliptic,
could be regarded as small. They may, therefore, be profitably treated by methods developed originally by the late E. W. Brown in his investigations of the stellar case of three bodies [15]; but his results
require an extension to incorporate the effects of higher eccentricities
which may be encountered in this connection.

   In contrast with the influence of the Sun, the attraction of the
Earth and the Moon on any rocket moving between them—such as the
American Pioneers, or the Russian Luniks—cannot be treated as a mere
perturbation. In point of fact, the proper dynamical formulation of the
motion of lunar probes must be sought within the framework of the restricted problem of three bodies—in which the rocket plays the role of
a mass-particle moving in the field of a gravitational dipole due to
the Earth and the Moon; and perturbed, in addition, by the attraction
of the Sun.

   It should, however, be stressed that the classical formulation of
the restricted problem of three bodies and its properties as investigated
by mathematicians of the nineteenth century—from Jacobi to Poincaré—
are scarcely adequate to serve as a basis for the computation of trajectories of lunar rockets in one important respect. In the classical
formulation of the problem, the orbit of the two finite bodies was regarded as circular, and their Keplerian angular velocity as constant.
Now, in actual fact, the relative orbit of the Moon around the Earth is
characterized by an eccentricity of $e = 0.0549$, which is too large for
its effects to be ignorable. Therefore, it becomes necessary to generalize the classical restricted problem to one in which at least the first
powers of e are consistently retained. Pioneer work performed in this

direction by Moulton [16] and his associates at the University of Chicago many years ago should be resumed, with particular attention to the properties of closed integrals of so generalized a problem. For instance, its vis-viva integral—and, therefore, all properties of the surfaces of zero velocity based upon it—will now become functions of the time. An investigation of their diverse properties offers an immediate and rewarding opportunity for a large amount of numerical work, which has not yet even begun.

What type of particle orbits are of primary interest in this connection? This depends entirely on the instrumentation and intended use of the respective rockets. If their aim were to be merely to reach the surface of the Moon, for instance, the initial conditions should evidently be such as to give as short a trajectory leading to its destination as is possible for given initial thrust. If, however, the rocket were a probe intended to monitor conditions prevailing in free space, it would obviously be of advantage to place it in a stable periodic orbit preferably at (or in the neighborhood of) any one of the five Lagrangian points. Because of the nonlinearity of our equations of motion, the initial conditions requisite for orbits of this type cannot, unfortunately, be established by any direct methods—and numerical integrations again offer the sole avenue of approach. A relatively large amount of numerical work has already been done on trajectories situated in the orbital plane of the two finite bodies describing circular orbits; but next to nothing is known about periodic space trajectories. Their investigation represents a powerful and timely challenge to the fastest computing machines of our time, and will obviously have to be carried quite far before even a rudimentary picture of the gravitational "navigation charts" in the sub-lunar space will begin to emerge from such efforts.

In conclusion of these brief remarks on some of the problems confronting us in celestial mechanics today, one point should perhaps be stressed. The dynamical problems which have, in recent years, become of such urgency and importance as a result of man's ability to launch rockets into space, have not been with us since yesterday. The cumulative effort of theoretical astronomers in the past 250 years have provided an extensive groundwork from which modern investigations can profitably depart; but because in the past generation or so the celestial mechanics rather ceased to be à la mode and had to yield its traditional place in educational curricula of our universities to other branches of astronomical science promising more immediate rewards, its methods and results are perhaps not as well known now as they should. This is, unfortunately, only too evident from a great number of recent contributions to this subject coming from the pens of physicists or engineers, whose work either duplicates that already available, or attempts to tackle it by methods which were tried before and discarded, for good reasons, in favor of alternative and more adequate approach. May I end by expressing a hope that this situation—and the lack of liaison between astronomers and physicists or engineers which it reflects—will be rectified in the near future for the benefit of the common cause?

REFERENCES

1. Cf., e.g., T. E. Sterne, Astron. Journ., 63, 81, 1958; B. Garfinkel, Astron. Journ., 63, 88, 1958; J. P. Vinti, Phys. Rev. Letters, 3, 8, 1959; and others.

2. For fuller details cf. pp. 63-67 of the forthcoming monograph on The Figures of Equilibrium of Celestial Bodies, by Z. Kopal, (Mathematics Research Center, U. S. Army, Publication No. 3), University of Wisconsin Press, Madison, 1960.

3. Cf., K. E. Bullen, Bull. Seism. Soc. Amer., 30, 235, 1940; 32, 19, 1942; as reproduced by J. A. Jacobs in Handb. der Phys., 47 (Geophysik I), Berlin 1956, pp. 372-373 (Tables 3 and 5).

4. F. L. Whipple, Astron. Journ., 63, 462, 1958.

5. Cf., e.g., R. Tomaschek, Handb. der Phys., 47, (Geophysik II), p. 812.

6. For relevant literature on this problem cf. M. V. Wilkes's monograph on Oscillations of the Earth's Atmosphere (Cambridge Monographs of Physics), Cambridge Univ. Press, 1949.

7. R. Jastrow and C. A. Pearse, Journ. Geophys. Res., 62, 413, 1957.

8. T. E. Sterne, Phys. of Fluids, 1, 165, 1958.

9. G. F. Schilling and T. E. Sterne, Journ. Geophys. Res., 64, 1, 1959.

10. H. E. LaGow and R. Horowitz, Phys. of Fluids, 1, 478, 1958.

11. L. G. Jacchia, Nature, 183, 526, 1662, 1959.

12. K. P. Chopra, Journ. Geophys. Res., 62, 143, 1957.

13. L. Kraus and K. M. Watson, Phys. of Fluids, 1, 480, 1958.

14. Cf., e.g., O. Jefimenko, Amer. Journ. of Phys., 27, 344, 1959.

15. E. W. Brown, Mon. Not. Roy. Astr. Soc., 97, 56, 62, 116, 388, 1936.

16. Cf. F. R. Moulton, Periodic Orbits, Washington 1920, Chapter VII (pp. 217-282).

Table 1

SOME CHARACTERISTICS OF THE SATELLITE ORBITS

Satellite	Date of Launching	Initial Distance		Period
		Apogee	Perigee	
1957 α : Sputnik I	1957 Oct. 4	950 km	225 km	96.2 min
1957 β : Sputnik II	Nov. 3	1670	240	103.7
1958 α : Explorer I	1958 Feb. 1	2540	368	114.9
1958 β : Vanguard I	Mar. 17	3965	652	134.3
1958 γ : Explorer III	Mar. 26	2800	188	115.9
1958 δ : Sputnik III	May 15	1880	241	105.9

Table 2

ORBITAL ACCELERATIONS PRODUCED BY
PERTURBATIONS OF DIFFERENT ORIGIN

(in absolute units)

Atmospheric drag	neutral: $(R^2/m)v^2\rho \sim 2 \times 10^{10} \rho$ cm/sec^2
	induction: ??
Rotational distortion	second-harmonic: $-1.08(R_\oplus/r^4)P_2(\nu)$
	fourth-harmonic: $0.0042(R_\oplus/r)^6 \, P_4(\nu)$
Tidal distortion	equilibrium: $\sim 10^{-12}(R_\oplus/r)^4$
	dynamical: $\sim 0.001(R_\oplus/r)^4$
Attraction by the	Sun: 0.0054
	Moon: 0.0033

Discussion of Paper Three

Dr. Musen: It is interesting to point out that in the development of lunar and solar perturbation the inclination does not present any problem because if we fix a number of harmonics in the development, then all coefficients are not series but polynomials with respect to $\sin \frac{i}{2}$. The real problem is the eccentricity, but if the satellite is pretty far from the moon, we shall have to take into consideration only long periodic terms. In this case the coefficients have simple form with respect to the eccentricities. One is $\frac{3}{2} e^2$ and the second is $\frac{5}{2} e^2$ so that for satellites of the type we have now, neither inclination nor eccentricity presented any problem as concerns the lunar and solar perturbations.

Dr. Kopal: This is true for intervals of time for which the expansions of the perturbation equations converge, but I think we could make a strong point at this stage that there is really no need to expand any of the perturbation equations in series. The perturbation equations are nonlinear, but offer no difficulty whatever to a numerical solution as they stand. In other words, what I feel astronomers should do is to depart from the time-honored practice of the nineteenth century where you started expanding the perturbations in series of the mean anomaly but to take the bull by the horns and solve the equations, nonlinear as they are, on a fast machine to see what comes out.

Dr. Musen: Yes, but the real trouble is a paralactic factor $\frac{a}{a'}$. Providing we do not have the resonance effects, it can make the convergence worse, but if the eccentricity is very large, and we cannot use time as an independent variable, then we can switch to eccentric anomaly and then no trouble with eccentricity arises at all, neither for long or for short periods.

May I ask you another question? What do you think about third harmonics? Some people discuss it, but their opinions are so different that I would just like to know what is your personal opinion?

Dr. Kopal: The question of the occurrence of the third harmonic or odd harmonics in the gravitational field of the earth or planets is one which has been somewhat of a skeleton in the closet of this particular branch of astronomical science. There is some direct evidence for it from gravimetric measurements forthcoming only in the past year. Many of you may have seen the recent announcements from Russia that the analysis of the gravimetric measurements made by the Soviet expedition during the IGY year in the Antarctic is bringing out the presence of the third harmonic in an analysis of the gravitational

acceleration of the surface of the Earth in a significant amount; and
if so, it will have to be taken into account also in our perturbing
function. Nobody (which includes the Russians) has so far advanced
any reasonable explanation as to what should be the cause of this
third harmonic. But different things can happen to the Earth. For
instance, one cannot rule out the possibility of material currents in
the Earth's core. It may be unsafe, for instance, to identify the center of gravity of the Earth constantly with the center of its geometrical symmetry for long periods of time. That motions must be present
in the core of the Earth we know from the existence of the magnetic
field. Now, if charged particles can move about, so can the neutral
ones; and if so, the occurrence of odd harmonics (and in particular
the third harmonic) might indeed be expected. The magnitude of the
coefficients reported by Kozyrev and other Russian observers of the
third harmonic would put its effects squarely in the class of the
second-order perturbations which we had on the blackboard. They
may, in fact, be comparable—if not larger—with the atmospheric
neutral drag at an altitude between 200 to 250 kilometers.

With respect to the time series, Dr. Musen, you have made your
point (which reflects fully, I should say, the classical astronomical
tradition of the past 200 years). I should, however, like to say that
it may be expedient for us to depart from our time-honored ways:
namely, to give up all the time expansions which started with Laplace
and integrate the equations numerically. After all, the machines
available to us at the present time take no exception whatever to the
nonlinearities such as the variational equations contain, and we can
integrate the time variation of all the elements taking them all properly into account. The expansions should agree with the outcome of
numerical integrations provided the time interval is short enough, and
what is "short enough" depends, of course, on the nature of each
specific perturbation.

Speaking of the third harmonic... before we get into any serious
argument as to its meaning, one should bring up the problem of the
fourth harmonic which has not been done so far. This constitutes a
second-order term; but to the best of my knowledge, no one has yet
gone to the trouble of evaluating this coefficient theoretically for a
given distribution of density in the Earth and making a consistent
determination of it jointly with the determination of the coefficient of
the second harmonic. The estimates of the fourth-harmonic coefficient used so far can at best be described as semi-empirical.

I have been cautioned by the chairman of this meeting to avoid
presenting any original results for lack of time; but since you mention
this point, and if I may have a couple of minutes more, I should like
now to call on those slides which we left out. I should just like to
show you the way we here at the Center go about determining these
two coefficients; and, in particular, that of the fourth harmonic.

Now, if we assume that the Earth behaves like a perfect fluid
(and on the time scale available to us, no matter what the viscosity
coefficient of the Earth may be, we have sufficient right to do so),

and assume the surface of the Earth to be of the form as given by equation (5-1) without the third harmonic (since we have no justification for it), it can be shown that the coefficient f_2 of $P_2(\nu)$ must obey to the second order in small quantities equation (5-20) which is a generalization of Clairaut's equation[*]. If you equate its left-hand side to zero alone, you have the well-known Clairaut's equation which has been tackled since 1743. But, its second order term as you see it here is new, and so are the boundary conditions as stated down there. It is a boundary-value problem with part of the conditions given inside and part given on the surface, and in these equations D is the factor through which the density enters; namely D is defined as a ratio of the local density at a distance from the center to the mean density of a sphere interior to it, and this depends on the internal structure of the Earth. All knowledge we possess of the internal structure of the Earth must, of course, come largely from seismology.

Now, the next slide will summarize the density distributions (due to Bullen) which we have used for this purpose. According to Bullen, one represents the most probable distribution of density inside the Earth, and the other the minimum distribution. You see, practically the sole uncertainty of the internal structure of the Earth pertains to the region immediately near the center, but as soon as we emerge from the inner core outside, the agreement of both curves is very good and the uncertainty small. If we adopt now these distributions of density for the Earth, the next slide will show the corresponding variation of the function D , which explicitly occurs in Clairaut's equation. We are just in the process of constructing the numerical solutions of this equation on the IBM 704 machine here at the Center. The final results are not available as yet, but should appear shortly in one of the forthcoming reports of the MRC.

Sticking my neck out a bit, and on the basis of partial numerical results obtained so far, I should say that I expect the coefficient of the fourth harmonic caused by the axial rotation of the Earth to be approximately 32 meters, as compared with that of the second harmonic amounting to 14 kilometers. When our present numerical work is completed, we shall for the first time have in our hands consistent determination of the coefficients of the second and fourth harmonic based on the same law of density distribution inside the Earth.

Dr. Lanczos: My question is only in connection with this second harmonic. In the classical theory, of course, we assume that the

---

[*] Reference was made, at this stage, by means of slides, to equations (5-20) and (5-21), together with their associated boundary conditions, as they stand on p. 70 of the speaker's recent monograph on The Figures of Equilibrium of Celestial Bodies, (Mathematics Research Center, U. S. Army, Publication No. 3), University of Wisconsin Press, Madison, 1960.

potential is expansible with coefficients that are time-dependent, but due to the daily rotation of the Earth, I would suppose that these expansion coefficients become functions of time. Did you take that into account?

Dr. Kopal: No, this has not been taken into account in this theory, on the assumption that the Earth behaves like an equilibrium fluid.

Dr. Lanczos: ...assuming that the Earth is a fluid body, but does not have rotational symmetry. . .

Dr. Kopal: If it does not, this is precisely where the third harmonic will come in, and the empirical evidence on the third harmonic based on metric measurements may bear this out. In fact, this may be one way of accounting for this harmonic.

Dr. Musen has referred to a matter which reveals another aspect of the mathematical no-man's land in our subject. Whenever we take into account the effects of tidal distortion—partial tides—then, of course, time enters immediately. This has so far not been done, although the departure of, say, the Pacific Ocean from an equilibrium form as a result of the passage of the Moon above it may cause deviations from it which are of the order of 10 meters or so—and, as a result, comparable in its gravitational effects with those of the fourth-order rotational harmonic distortion. The tidal effects are bound to prove extremely complicated, and many of our present colleagues choose to refer to their accumulative effect as the "gravitational noise".

Dr. Shanks: Could you say again what is the relative magnitude of the two so-called atmospheric drags?

Dr. Kopal: In order to answer this question, let us return again to the approximate expressions compiled in Table 2 as shown on one of the previous slides. If the magnitude of the coefficient R^2/m is taken to be 100 (which constitutes a fair approximation, though it may vary from satellite to satellite) and a (quasi-circular) velocity v adopted as 8 km/sec, the whole factor representing atmospheric drag comes out to be about $2 \times 10^{10} \rho$ cm/sec^2 . Its numerical magnitude will of course be controlled by the density ρ which diminishes very rapidly with height. Now the observed response of motion of some satellites to certain manifestations of solar activity have indicated, tentatively, that the electromagnetic drag may impede the motions of these satellites about as much as simple atmospheric resistance does at altitudes between 200-250 kms. It is, furthermore, probable that the electromagnetic drag does not diminish with height with the same rapidity as the neutral drag (i. e., the density); but as long as we do not know more about the true cause of the electromagnetic drag on the satellites, it is perhaps still rather premature to speculate much about the behavior of its effect with height.

Dr. Shanks: Was it comparable with the neutral drag?

Dr. Kopal: No, for both Sputnik III and Vanguard I, it was large in comparison with neutral drag.

Aeroelasticity

I am going to give a broad-brush picture of one of the new hybrid fields—aeroelasticity. We know that recently there have been many of these. We hear of magnetohydrodynamics, aerothermochemistry and various other such fields. The truth of it is that the title "aeroelasticity" is too limited. It should be so put together that it does include other very important effects. The earliest interest in such effects was immediately after the flight of aircraft at the beginning of the century when various instabilities were experienced in flight vehicles. The first investigations assumed however that the aircraft was an infinitely rigid body that Routh's laws of dynamics, rigid body dynamics, would hold, and that the primary dynamic mechanism was associated with the gravitational field. However, when higher speeds of flight were reached, it was found that there were various mechanisms referred to as torsional divergence, flutter, control reversal, all of which involved deformations of the aircraft structural elements coupled with the unsteady aerodynamic or quasi-steady aerodynamic effects that were induced.

The influence of the other portions of the wing and body could be approximated by assuming that the system is semi-rigid; that is, there is no distortion or change of shape of the chord-wise section, and that we can picture here the system, suspended as from two springs, at zero angle of attack with an incoming flow field, say, of undisturbed velocity V at a large distance from the aircraft.

If the system is given a slight angle of attack, it is possible that there might be an over-balance of the aerodynamic pitching moment over the restoring forces of the spring system. This is commonly referred to as torsional divergence of the wing. However, what is more apt to happen if the system is displaced and then released at the low-speeds, is that amplitude versus time is a decaying oscillation. However, as the speed increases, we find that we reach a critical speed where oscillations are maintained, and beyond that a very explosive catastrophic mechanism takes place. The phenomenon referred to is flutter. What is actually happening there, is that the motion of the system is creating vorticity that is shed into the air stream. This vorticity of course quickly diffuses. The oscillations also send out accoustic radiation from the body surface, and both result in feed-back mechanisms. The vorticity shed is continuously inducing effects on the wing as it is convected downstream, and the radiation of course takes time to propagate from one point of the system to another.

The earliest analytical investigation of this phenomenon was by Theodorsen in this country and Kuster in Germany. There it was assumed that at low speeds thickness effects could be neglected. This is quite true in the subsonic range, and a treatment which separated so-called noncirculatory and circulatory effects so that the impulsive motion was determined on the one hand by suitable distribution of sources and sinks, and the creation of a vortex street concentrated in a thin region of discontinuity was evaluated for sinusoidal motion at the tip. The result of this was to obtain, instead of the theoretical lift, the lift multiplied by a complex expression f + ig whose real and imaginary parts f and g were complicated functions of Bessel functions of various orders.

Based on this type of analysis, flutter analyses were performed which enabled one to predict fairly well the behavior of aircraft in the lower speed range. However, with the introduction of high speed aircraft during and immediately after World War II, various investigators became aware of the fact that compressibility effects were important as well as nonlinear effects. However, in all investigations to make the problem at all tractable, it was assumed that dissipation mechanisms in the flow field could be neglected except for, again, this very thin region of discontinuity in the wake. The assumption then was that there existed a velocity potential which gave the vector velocity. The resulting nonlinear equation

$$(1 - \frac{u^2}{a^2})\frac{\partial^2 \phi}{\partial x^2} + (1 - \frac{v^2}{a^2})\frac{\partial^2 \phi}{\partial y^2} + (1 - \frac{w^2}{a^2})\frac{\partial^2 \phi}{\partial z^2}$$

$$- \frac{2uv}{a^2}\frac{\partial^2 \phi}{\partial x \partial y} - \frac{2vw}{a}\frac{\partial^2 \phi}{\partial y \partial z} - \frac{2wu}{a^2}\frac{\partial^2 \phi}{\partial z \partial x} = \frac{1}{a^2}\frac{\partial^2 \phi}{\partial t^2} \quad ,$$

where a here of course is the local speed of sound. To again make the problem available for analysts, this system of equations was linearized obtaining a system that took this form:

$$(1) \qquad \frac{1}{a_\infty^2}(\frac{\partial}{\partial t} + U\frac{\partial}{\partial x})^2 \phi = \nabla^2 \phi$$

where a_∞ is the speed of sound in the undisturbed region, U is the velocity of flight where it is assumed now that the airfoil has zero angle of attack. This equation has been the subject of many investigations since the end of the 1930's. I believe one of the first to attempt to solve this for the case of the oscillating airfoil was Possio

in Italy. There have been quite a few investigators in this country including Reissner, Biot and quite a few others, and of course a large
number of investigators in the Soviet.

By assuming a simple harmonic motion, period $2\pi/\omega$, the system is considerably simplified, and combining terms, one obtains this
equation involving the Mach number in the undisturbed field:

$$(1-M_\infty^2)\frac{\partial^2\phi}{\partial x^2} + \frac{\partial^2\phi}{\partial y^2} + \frac{\partial^2\phi}{\partial z^2} - \frac{2i\omega}{a_\infty^2}\frac{\partial\phi}{\partial x} + \frac{U^2}{a_\infty^2}\phi = 0 \ .$$

By introducing an affine transformation and a Lorentz transformation,
that is, assuming that $\phi = f(x', y, z)e^{i\omega\alpha x'}$ where $\alpha = \dfrac{U}{a^2\beta}$, β being
$\sqrt{1-M_\infty^2}$, a simple differential equation is obtained in the wave equa-
tion form:

$$\frac{\partial^2 f}{\partial x^2} + \frac{\partial^2 f}{\partial y^2} + \frac{\partial^2 f}{\partial z^2} + \frac{\omega^2}{a_\infty^2\beta}f = 0 \ .$$

This equation has been solved making use of various devices. Possio
was the first to study this, developing an integral equation form for
the solution. If there are any numerical analysts who
have been acquainted with this problem who might make comments, I
think this would be appreciated. The integral equation has singularities at the various locations of sources of disturbance. The treatment
of this problem for high-speed flow (supersonic flow) however, becomes
considerably simpler. If we considered, for example, a delta wing,
what I show here would hold for any shape vehicle flying at speed V ,
or relative speed V , such that if this normal component of velocity
is less than the speed of sound at infinity (the undisturbed speed of
sound) one finds that there exist solutions of the differential equation
that take the form

$$\phi = \frac{W(\xi, \eta)}{2\pi b\beta}e^{-\bar\omega(x-\xi)}\frac{\cos(\frac{\bar\omega}{M}R)}{R}$$

where W is downwash and I have nondimensionalized now the system
where we have coordinates y, η or x, ξ . I have nondimensionalized
with reference to the dimension 2 times b where b is the major semi-
chord. The downwash then at any location ξ, η results in a velocity
potential on the body which takes the form shown here where the parameter

$$\bar\omega = \frac{2kM^2}{M^2-1} \ ;$$

R is an effective radius, which takes the form

$$R = \sqrt{(x-\xi)^2-(M^2-1)(y-\eta)^2}$$

and k here is a ratio of frequency times this maximum semi-chord
divided by velocity. In subsonic flow, this k is the critical parameter of unsteady airfoil phenomena where it is actually a ratio of the

time for a particle to traverse the airfoil to the period of oscillations.
When k is small, unsteady effects are small, so-called reduced frequency. However, in this case our measure of unsteadiness involves
a function of k and the Mach number.

The boundary conditions I neglected to mention for any of these
problems is that the wake has the width of the body. The pressure
jump through the body vanishes at the trailing edge, or, what is essentially the same, the velocity of flow tangential to the trailing edge
is finite, the so-called Kutta condition; that there are singularities at
the leading edge that are of the order of the distance from the leading
edge; and that the usual Sommerfeld radiation conditions hold—that the
disturbances are outgoing and vanish at infinity. I believe that is the
whole family—plus the condition that the normal velocity (in this case
assuming a flat plate) at the body $\frac{\partial \phi}{\partial z}$ is equal to the downwash of the
particles at the body. It can be shown, assuming that there is no dis-
tortion of the particle path, that W for amplitude of motion z from
the steady state takes this form

$$\frac{\partial \phi}{\partial z}\bigg|_{x=0} = W = \frac{\partial z}{\partial t} + V\frac{\partial z}{\partial x} .$$

In other words, assuming two motions normal to the body, one due to
the motion of the airfoil that is oscillating and the other due to the
local slope at the position of the particle, the pressure jump across
the body for this linearized situation can be shown to be

$$p = -2\rho \frac{\partial \phi}{\partial t} + V\frac{\partial \phi}{\partial x}$$

and this is due to the fact that ϕ is a symmetrical function relative
to the z normal direction of the airfoil.

By combining now the total pressure due to the known oscillatory
motion z which gives us our downwash and obtaining this pressure
from this solution ϕ , one can obtain the total lift and moment on the
airfoil. For this particular case where the normal velocity component
is larger than the speed of sound so that this component is also supersonic, we find that the influences of this downwash at any point ξ, η
are limited to the intersection of a Mach cone which has slope that is
larger than that of the leading edge, so that what is felt on one side
of the airfoil is not transmitted to the other side. Calculations of
complete lift moment for various modes of motion of such an airfoil
have been carried out and have been the basis of various aeroelastic
investigations.

The difficulty occurs however in supersonic flight when this condition is not satisfied. Then we have the zone of influence of such a
nature that disturbances downwash at a point ξ, η on one side of the
wing will feed to the other side of the wing. Investigators in the USSR
and Evard in this country have satisfactorily treated this problem where
a fictitious membrane having the slope of this Mach line is introduced
a fictitious disturbance, that is downwash, is distributed on these

membranes, and integral equations are developed (which become fairly simple for steady state case but quite complex for the unsteady)
which enable one to carry through this complete calculation.

However, when we reach the higher speeds of flight, these linear
methods are no longer applicable because we can catalog the conditions
for linearity. We must have the following: that all perturbation parameters are small compared to the ambient or steady state. In the case
of the perturbation velocities, this requires that the perturbation components u, v, w are not only small when compared to the relative undisturbed motion of the fluid, but also must be small when compared
to the speed of sound in the undisturbed field, and also the difference
of flight speed and speed of sound. Even for small motions, this lin-
earization will break down. In this case, in the transonic range and
in that case in the hypersonic. If you recall, the measure of unsteadiness for the linearized system took the form

$$\bar{\omega} = \frac{2k\omega^2}{M^2-1} \quad .$$

This gives us the picture that even for extremely small values of the
reduced frequency as proportional to the frequency of oscillation, when
Mach number is close to 1, serious unsteady effects can take place.
By a careful dimensional analysis of the equations, Tsien, Lin and
Reissner concluded that in the linear wave equation (1) there should
be added to the left-hand side a term

$$\frac{\gamma+1}{2} \frac{\partial\phi}{\partial x} \frac{\partial^2\phi}{\partial x^2} \quad .$$

Even for small oscillations in the transonic unsteady case, such a
term should be included, where γ is, of course, the ratio of specific
heats, c_p to c_v .

In the transonic case, in addition to the mechanisms we described,
we have the influence of mixed flow regions and such phenomena occur-
ring as so-called aileron buzz. This appears to be the result of a
coupling between the existence of a shock wave on the airfoil, the
interaction of the shock with the boundary layer, and disturbances
which are being fed to the shock and suddenly carried downstream,
so that when this phenomenon is observed, there is a buzzing of the
aileron or control surface, and at the same frequency, but out of phase,
an oscillation of the shock.

This in the past has had serious consequences on the flight limits
of high-speed aircraft. In the hypersonic range where we do get perturbations that are small compared to velocity of flight, we do get this
situation where flight speed is so great compared to speed of sound
that the perturbations are of the order or greater than sound speed.
Fortunately people like Wally Hayes, Lighthill and others have exam-
ined by, again, dimensional analysis the equations of motion in this
regime at sufficient distances away from the nose shocks, and have
found that, because the Mach lines are quite flat, the very large gradients in the flow field are in the direction normal to the body as

compared to gradients in the direction of flow. The consequence of this is that one can throw away all derivates in the equations of motion other than those in this normal direction, and there is obtained a one-dimensional set of equations which is exactly the same equations as one finds in piston theory. As a consequence, this simplification has been referred to as piston theory. The physical mechanism here if we picture a wedge with the flow approaching the wedge, we imagine columns of fluid as they approach the airfoil. Of course, here we should be neglecting the effects in the vicinity of the nose region, but it appears something of this sort. There is a piston that is moving in this direction. Now, in our particular situation, the motion of that piston is our downwash W. On the surface it has, of course, the initial slope of the body to contend with plus the mean oscillatory motion of the airfoil plus the dynamic slope—the slope corresponding to oscillations. Since these equations correspond to the simple Earnshaw piston theory, one obtains as do you from that theory a simple expression for the pressure: the ratio pressure to pressure at infinity is equal to

$$\frac{p}{p_\infty} = [1 + \frac{\gamma-1}{2} \frac{W}{a_\infty}]^{\frac{2\gamma}{\gamma-1}} \ .$$

Lighthill in his application of this has argued that if we expand this to its first three terms, usual complications of entropy effects can be neglected, and one obtains an expansion that looks something of this order:

$$\frac{p}{p_\infty} = 1 + \gamma \frac{W}{a_\infty} + \frac{\gamma(\gamma+1)}{4} \left(\frac{W}{a_\infty}\right)^2 + \frac{\gamma(\gamma+1)}{12} \left(\frac{W}{a_\infty}\right)^3 \ .$$

One can show that this last term should not be included in the expansion, but, however, Lighthill has pointed out for engineering type accuracy that this might be a useful addition. The result of this is that one does not get involved at all in the solution of such a problem, but one can put directly into this equation the expression for downwash including the effect of thickness.

In comparing the results one obtains from this extremely simple theory, to more elaborate theories (for example, W. P. Jones in Great Britain has studied high speed flow over a double convex affair of this sort and the pressure distributions obtained show extremely good agreement).

Up until this point we have been particularly concerned with unsteady phenomena such as flutter. Other mechanisms that fall in the category "aeroelasticity" are those involving forced mechanisms, but although these are forced since the forcing does not affect the deformation of the body, in addition to the forcing functions, these same unsteady aerodynamic effects are felt. For example, one may consider the influence of atmospheric turbulence on a flexible airplane or missile, the influence of sharp-edged gusts on such a system, and, more recently, the influence of such things as aerodynamic noise.

Of course, there has been a great deal of concern about mechanisms of jet noise for the mixing in the jet creates intense noise fields that Lighthill has shown behave as Mach number to the fourth power in intensity. However, in Lighthill's theory that dipoles are created by such a mixing region, he assumed that his evaluation of them must be made at large distances from reflecting bodies such as the jet body itself. He has pointed out that the presence of a sounding board such as the wall of a missile could have a large effect on the intensity of the noise.

Now, he was concerned primarily with the transmission of noise from the mixing region out into the atmosphere, but recently there has been concern with the problem of transmission of noise into bodies. Assuming this is the body of the fuselage of a supersonic airplane or just the body of a high speed missile, we know that we have boundary layer mechanisms of a fluctuating nature attached to the surface of the body. These fluctuations create intense noise fields which transmit through the wall of the body, affect instrumentation, and of course in transports would have a serious effect on occupants of the body.

Analyses have been started on such a system where it has been supposed that the same equations of motion used by such people as Lees and Lin for the study of stability of compressible boundary layers could be employed in the study of transmission of noise into the interior of such a body. The argument is this: we can assume that the motion of an assumed elastic shell is sinusoidal. The solutions that have always been assumed in the case of the Orr-Sommerfeld equations for incompressible flow and for the compressible case by Lees and Lin and others are assumed to have a simple wave form.

Now the approach to the problem is to take the nonlinear equations of hydrodynamics, the Navier-Stokes equations, to linearize them but with the introduction of variations in the steady state parameters, velocity in this direction, density, pressure, temperature, etc. If one writes down these equations, we have essentially the equations of Lees and Lin, and assumes—not as they did that the wall is infinitely rigid—but that we have a flexible wall with a wavy amplitude, one can make use of the same solutions of Lees and Lin and use it as a means of coupling together the motion of the fluid, the wall, and (if there is an interior accoustic mechanism) the accoustic mechanism. Then, making use of the Lees-Linn type solutions, introduce then a forcing function which is the turbulant eddy travelling through the boundary layer. Estimates have shown that the intensity of this noise field is of the order of what one obtains from this jet mixing region when you reach Mach numbers of 3, 4 etc.

One of the purposes for my being here is to try to indicate what fields of interest there are to the mathematical analyst and numerical analyst in this field of aeroelasticity. Looking to the future, one has to conjecture a great deal. One problem that Garabedian and Lieberstein had fairly successfully handled was that of the detached shock at high speed flow, stagnation point here, sonic line here, and then flow continuing this direction. It is my understanding not much has been done on this problem when the body is at an angle of attack. The question arises for this oscillatory case: is it possible to carry further their type of solution to include the oscillatory behavior of this system?

Another serious situation we are confronted with at hypersonic flight is that tests that are made in wind tunnels at hypersonic speeds indicate that here we have a shock very close to the body, but viscous effects are predominant for quite a distance away from the body. It may very well be that in studying unsteady behavior—aeroelastic behavior—of such a system, the neglect of dissipation mechanisms that we introduced can no longer be tolerated. Further types of mechanisms going beyond this aeroelasticity combination might very well include chemical reactions at the surfaces, ablation processes, and here one possibility comes to mind. Many years ago Theodore von Karman studied the wavy sand patterns one finds on beaches and of course on deserts, including the viscous boundary layer effects. However, in pictures I have seen recently of slabs of metal that have been subjected to high speed flows, one sees something quite similar to this so that there is a waviness on the surface. The feeling is that just as there was a critical wave length involved here, there may very well be on the body surface, and since our unsteady effects include two terms—one of this form of frequency, and the other velocity times the slope of a wave number—one might find that there are unsteady phenomena that are seriously affected by this melting situation.

One can think up various other types of coupling. One that appeals to everyone now is that of magnetohydrodynamics. There have been recent studies attempting to find the interaction of a fast travelling body containing an ionized layer (plasma) with an incoming electromagnetic field. The field has to be strong enough, of course, if signals want to be transmitted or if they want to influence in any way the system. It has been shown by crude calculations that a good deal of this energy is dumped at the shock. How exact this is, I am not sure—but the dumping of this energy causes a distortion of this shock wave and the question is—if this is coming in at some angle to the direction of flight, there will be an axisymmetrical distortion of this shock front. The problem of coupling between these two fields may become significant, and may be significant in these unsteady problems I have discussed.

NOTE

[*] This version of Dr. Arnold's lecture was made from a tape recording. It was not finally reviewed by the author.

Discussion of Paper Four

Dr. Pan: Dr. Arnold mentioned at the beginning of the talk this word "aeroelasticity" may be too restrictive, and this brings to my thought a problem that currently concerns the General Electric Company in the reactor design for submarine power plans, and there is constant need for the Navy to have a propulsion unit that is very quiet for obvious reasons. It seems that the military value of a submarine is very much reduced if it is noisy. There is the desire to minimize mechanical rotating machinery noise. So here is a possible scheme to go to, and I believe it opens up another field worthy of attention. If the coolant for the reactor is driven by the natural circulation phenomenon instead of by pumps, the fuel elements of the reactor have to be cooled. While the reactor is delivering power to propel the ship, the heat it discards to the coolant also causes the coolant to circulate. At the same time, the captain is trying to dictate the motion of the ship. How does this motion of the ship interact with the natural circulation problem, and in turn affect the performance of the reactor?

Dr. Arnold: I know the Navy has coined its own word. They refer to this as "hydroelasticity". But this problem of boundary layer noise is of serious consequence to the Navy. The impedances of the liquid are, of course, much greater than that of air, and they find that their high-speed submarines are not extremely useful because of the noise created by the boundary layer so intense that it masks out all other signals that it would like to hear.

Dr. Bueckner: What is your experience with possible flutter in steam turbines?

Dr. Arnold: The problem of steam turbines is the following. I have had some experience with the General Electric Company on their steam turbines. As I pointed out here, when we are close to Mach number 1, we can get very intense nonlinear and serious unsteady effects. Now, the steam turbine people have always argued that the mass ratio (and this is if one takes a flat plate and creates a cylinder of air around it or whatever the medium is) that the measure or ratio of inertia of gas to inertia of the body is, by this simple formula, the mass of this circle would be $\dfrac{\pi \rho_g b^2}{M}$ to the mass of the body. The steam used in these steam turbines is of such low intensity that this is extremely negligible. However, analysis has shown that in the subsonic range due to these nonlinear effects and increased influence of unsteadiness, that there is a possibility of a serious flutter situation. Here I think is a field where the numerical analyst could have some fun. Most of these rotating machinery problems are treated as cascade problems where one has a system of buckets that can be pictured to be in a cascade of this form. The difficult problem of numerical analysis of the single blade is setting up a finite difference scheme that includes enough of the gas in the far neighborhood of the body. Now, here there is a possibility of breaking this up into two problems because of the infinite extent of this cascade one can assume that what is experienced is experienced in the sinusoidal manner. In the direction of this cascade, a numerical analysis could then be made for anyone of these cells and then, doing a similar thing that was done in the supersonic case with subsonic leading edge, one could introduce fictitious membranes here to obtain boundary conditions corresponding to known parameters and then tie these into analytical solutions away from the cascade. Now, something has been started on this, but there are difficult problems because of singularities of leading edges, and things of that sort, but I think that this is a problem that should be pursued a great deal further.

Dr. Bueckner: How do you take care of the cover band of tie wires?

Dr. Arnold: The aerodynamic incidence on tie wires is, of course, a difficult situation to handle. However, the tie wires that feed from one blade to another in themselves introduce a great deal of mechanical coupling. If it weren't for these tie wires the only coupling between these buckets or blades would be through aerodynamics, but with the tie wires there is direct rigidity coupling from one blade to another, and this is adequately taken care of.

Operations Research

I am to discuss a field which differs considerably from those already treated in this conference, and it might be well for me to define my terms. An operation is a pattern of activity of men—often of men and machines—which is goal-oriented, usually is repetitive and which is carried out according to predetermined rules of operation. A bombing operation is a typical military example, the operation of a factory is an industrial one and automobile traffic in a city street is a municipal example. Operations research is the scientific study of operations.

Operations are more amenable to the techniques of physical science than are most social activities. Because of their repetitive nature and because of the usual presence of equipment, they can be measured quantitatively, in terms of probability and expected values, and they can be experimented with. Because the goals of the operation can usually be stated quantitatively, it is appropriate to express the results of operational measurements in terms of mathematical models. Once the models have been tested by experiment, they can be used to predict the behavior of the operation under changed conditions and to revise rules of operation so as to produce optimal results.

A wide variety of operations have been studied in the past twenty years, since the beginning of operations research; they show a wide variety of external form, but have revealed many similarities of basic behavior. It appears that most operations are combinations of a relatively small number of unit operations, for each of which a mathematical model has been devised. These models must be worked out in more detail than has been yet possible, if we are to take the next step, to fit them together into theories representing more complex operations.

To take examples from the industrial field, we can follow a manufactured item from the mine to the retail store. Even before the mining operation one must find the ore or the oil or whatever the raw material is. Not much active operations research has gone into this kind of problem—except in petroleum prospecting—but it should be obvious that the unit operation of search will be a basic ingredient. Going on to the mining operation itself, one finds a number of unit operational constituents; maintenance, man-power allocation and stock-pile management, to name a few, which have similarities of pattern with related problems in other kinds of operations. There are of course a number of problems unique to the mining operation, such as those related to safety, which require study, but even here there are similarities in pattern to other fields.

In following our raw material to the factory we next can mention the general operation of transportation, with its typical unit operations of routing and scheduling, as well as the already encountered ones such as maintenance. Then of course there are the very complex operations of manufacture, involving production lines, allocation and maintenance problems and inventory management. The operation of distribution of the manufactured article involves the unit operations of inventory, of routing and scheduling, which we have already mentioned. The sales operation brings in some new types, related to the directly competitive nature of the operation, which use game theory in some of their mathematical models. Encompassing all of these operations are activities which link them all; communications operations and those of financial control.

Many other general types of operations have been studied. In each case they are analyzable into unit operations, many of which are already familiar. In military operations the unit operation of search, search for an enemy submarine by aircraft or by ship's sonar, search for an enemy plane by an anti-aircraft missile system, and so on, is an important element. Search theory, up to now, has been developed most energetically in connection with military operations, though, as I mentioned earlier, it has potential applications elsewhere. Game theory, basic to the mathematics of competitive operations, is also more developed in connection with military operations, though it might have possible applications in police operations. The problems of military logistics, on the other hand, are practically identical with those of commercial distribution (not sales).

In the study of all of these complex operations the research worker analyzes the behavior into unit operations, just as the scientist analyzing a complex physical system breaks it down into mechanical, electrical, hydraulic and other elements, for each of which he has an appropriate theoretical model. Unit operations which have been studied in some detail include those of search, of inventory control, of maintenance, of routing, of allocation of resources, and of competitive action. In each of these cases, and even more in other cases, progress is slowed because of incomplete development of the appropriate mathematical model. In no case do we have a theory nearly as well developed as are those of classical mechanics or of electromagnetic phenomena, for example. Basic mathematical theorems for many operational models are not yet developed and, even when the existence proofs are known, the algorithms which could attain actual solutions are missing. A great deal of mathematical work, of a high order, is needed.

As an example, consider a basic search problem* for a moment, that of the search for an enemy unit, such as ship or surfaced submarine, by a radar-equipped plane. We may know something as to its whereabouts and motion, which can be expressed in terms of a probability distribution—it is more likely to be here than there—for instance. We wish to distribute our search effort—the tracks of our search planes—so as to discover the ship with the least effort—the smallest number of flying hours—or we may wish to maximize our chance of discovery for a given amount of effort. Geometrically it is a question of placing a band, representing the search track of the plane, with its range of visibility, on the sea's surface so that the band "covers" the most likely locations of the searched-for target.

I think you will agree that this is not a simple problem; you can probably see that the classical calculus of variations has very little to contribute to its solution. Boundary conditions of an unfamiliar sort intrude. An essential part of the problem is the continuity of the search band—the plane must fly a continuous track. It is not clear whether the answer to the two problems mentioned, discovery for minimal expected effort or optimal chance of discovery for a given length of track, are always the same. Indeed, when the estimated probability of location of the target has several peaks, representing regions where the target is more likely to be, it is not certain that a solution is always unique. And, when one adds estimates of probable motion of the target, algorithms for obtaining usable solutions are practically non-existent.

Turning to another type of unit operation, that involving competition, the basic model here is game theory. Game theory is farther along in its development than search theory, but no one would argue that the field is worked out. In fact a great deal of further basic work will be necessary before game theory will be of much practical help in solving the problems which arise in sales operations. The cases which arise when there is a continuous distribution of strategies, as with competitive advertising for a closed market, are still untouched, for example.

The problem of allocation of effort enters into many operating questions. Some of the simplest can be solved by the methods of linear programming, those concerned with transportation, routing, for instance, and those encountered in scheduling production in an oil refinery. But linear programming is appropriate only when the payoff is a linear function of the variables and when the operational limitations can all be expressed as definite, linear functions of these same variables. If any of the limits are stochastic our present methods are cumbersome and may be inappropriate. These restrictions severely reduce the range of usefulness of linear programming, for one can rarely predict operational limits with precision. What is needed is an equivalent of linear programming when the equations for the limitations on the system must be expressed in terms of probabilities. Such an extension of the theory may also help solve the general search problems.

As a third example, I can mention those problems where the dynamics of the operation is of importance. Many operational systems are subject to forces which are stochastic in nature. Some of these are external forces; the varying demands for goods or fluctuating supplies, or the effects of enemy action, for example. Some of the "forces" acting on the system are the consequence of the rules of operation, laid down by management; the rules for replenishment of inventory, for routing of transportation or the tactical doctrine governing military action; these could be called internal forces. What is needed is a dynamical theory; indicating how an operational system responds to these external and internal forces, so that one can work out which set of operating rules, which internal forces, will make the system perform, on the average, as desired.

In a surprisingly large number of cases the appropriate mathematical model is that of a Markov process. One can often represent the dynamical behavior by expressing the time derivatives of the probabilities, that the system is in various possible states, in terms of transition rates from state i to state j . Simple examples of this mathematical model are encountered in queuing theory and in inventory control theory. More complex operational dynamics can be worked out when we are able to extend the theory. Here the problem is chiefly that of devising algorithms for obtaining specific solutions for specific Markov processes, though a more complete study of the general differences in behavior corresponding to different types of Markov matrices would be of great value.

For each of the unit operations I have mentioned, and for others too, there is need for basic research in extending the appropriate mathematical models. But there is also great opportunity for the application of digital computers. I need not discuss the obvious use of computers for working out specific theoretical solutions. Most operational systems are complex enough to be beyond representation in simple analytic terms; specific solutions must be expressed in terms of many numbers, and the digital machine is the appropriate way of getting them. Nor do I need to do more than mention the use of machines in processing the data required to adjust the mathematical model to fit the operation under study. But I do wish to spend some time discussing the somewhat paradoxical usefulness of digital computers in carrying out operational experiments.

Operations research is an experimental science, just as physics and chemistry are. Before we can develop mathematical models which simulate an operation we must learn by controlled experiment just what it is we are simulating. At least as much time and ingenuity go into the experimental aspects of operations research as go into the theoretical aspects.

But in most operations, it is quite difficult to persuade the boss of an operation to experiment with it; there are questions of the morale of the people involved and there is also the difficulty that experimentation usually reduces the efficiency of the operation for the duration of the experiment. Consequently, though it is often possible to

experiment on the unit operations, which make up the whole, it is
nearly always forbidden to experiment with the entire system under
study. You can imagine the reaction of a military staff if it were proposed to try out a completely new form of landing operation, or the
response of a bank president to a suggestion that a new system of
routing and recording of withdrawals and deposits be tried out for a
month! We can, by the expenditure of much effort, obtain a good idea
of the behavior of the elements of the operation and of the stochastic
nature of the various external forces acting on the system, but we
usually are not allowed to try out the effects of new operating rules,
linking the elements together into a complete operating system.

In many cases the number of unit operations making up the whole
are sufficiently large, and their interactions are sufficiently complex,
so that a purely theoretical solution is wellnigh impossible initially.
Most operations are too complex to be able to work out on paper all
the possibilities. Here, it seems to me, is an opportunity for digital
computers. Once the behavior of the unit operations and of the external forces is known experimentally, these behaviors can be simulated
by the computing machine and their interactions can be programmed so
that the machine will simulate the behavior of the operation as a whole.
We can introduce the various stochastic forces by Monte Carlo methods,
we can program in the various rules of operation which interconnect the
elements and we can have the machine tabulate the results in a way
which is most easily understood by the operating manager, so he can
see that the machine is actually simulating the operation as presently
constituted and how it will change if new rules are applied.

I believe such simulation is a powerful tool for operational experiment. I believe it should be used as experiments are usually used,
to help us develop improved mathematical models of the operation as a
whole, rather than as a means of computing the final answer. In nearly every case where we have used a machine to simulate an operation
we have learned a great deal about the general behavior of the operation, what forces are important, and what have negligible effect, where
bottlenecks are most likely to occur, and many other aspects of internal
dynamics. In many cases the simulation has suggested analytic methods of solution, and our final solutions have seldom been obtained by
Monte Carlo methods. Nevertheless, the machine simulation has been
necessary, since simulation has been the only way we could carry out
the experimentation needed to perfect the mathematical model.

Let me illustrate by mentioning three of the simulations which
have been carried out on the IBM 704 at the M.I.T. Computation Center.
The first is a fairly simple one, except for the size of the operation.
It is a study of the spare parts supply of Army Ordnance, conducted by
the M.I.T. Operations Research Center. The supply system of Army
Ordnance is one of the largest supply systems in the world. There is
a sequence of supply levels, the several main depots in this country,
the smaller depots, some abroad; these in turn supplying the supply
stations for the various forces. The flow of supplies is fairly straightforward; requests come to the supply sergeant, who satisfies them from

stock, if possible; from time to time he requests replenishment from
a depot, which in turn replenishes from another depot or from the
manufacturer. There are rules governing the size of the replenishment order, where it is sent and how it is related to the size of inventory remaining.

We studied data on primary demands for spare parts for five
years of operation, to determine the statistics of the demand fluctuations. The system handles many thousands of kinds of items, but we
found less than fifty different types, in regard to size, value, demand
rate, and variance of demand rate. We then simulated these demands
on the 704, programmed in the rules for replenishment at each supply
level, included the variable time delays in shipment and in factory
production, and ran the machine as the equivalent of the system, print-
ing out inventory levels at the supply points, shipments, and such important items as unsatisfied demands, for each equivalent week of
operation. An equivalent year of operation took a few minutes on the
machine, so we could make quite a few experiments without using up
too much machine time.

The theory of inventory management has been sufficiently developed so that one can compute, analytically, for a single depot,
what size inventory is necessary to reduce expected fraction of time
stock is out to a predetermined level, once the statistical nature of
the demand and the replenishment are specified. What the analytical
theory cannot yet do is to determine how the internal interactions of
a system of depots, with interconnected demands and replenishments,
will affect the behavior of the individual parts of the system. This is
what the simulation has helped us to understand. We first simulated
the system as it has been run, with the demands and operating rules
as they were for the past five years, to make certain that the machine
program did simulate the reactions and fluctuations of the recorded behavior. Then we tried a number of other sets of rules of operation, to
see how they reduced the fraction of stock-out time and changed the
pattern of factory replenishment orders. We also tested for sensitivity
by changing the statistical pattern of demands. The distribution in
time of demands for some items, incidentally, is far from the completely
random, or Poisson, distribution.

These runs gave us some ideas as to how a mathematical model
of the whole system could be devised; these ideas suggested further
trial runs with other rules, and so on. In other words, we have used
the simulations exactly as we would have used operational experiments,
if we had been allowed to experiment. Only the simulations could be
carried out much more quickly and with very considerably less trouble.

We also found that these simulations were an excellent means
of selling our ideas to management. The records produced by the simulations could be printed in a form familiar to those running the actual
operation. When the machine duplicated the past operation the records
showed familiar behavior; depots running out of supplies, recognizable
delays in shipment and so on. When the machine ran with other rules
of operation they could see how specific troubles were alleviated,

how much more stock was provided in various places, and how this increase would reduce stock-out time in crucial areas. We found that simulation, properly recorded, could demonstrate our findings and recommendations to management with a realism which no set of equations or other mathematical reasoning could achieve.

Another kind of operation which has been simulated on the 704 has been automobile traffic. The behavior of traffic, with all its variability of driver reaction, is a very complex operation. We felt we should work out the simplest kind of system first, in order to get experience. The simplest example we could think of was that of one-lane traffic, where every car follows the one ahead, with no turning out for passing, such as occurs in traffic tunnels. Luckily the Port of New York Authority has been keeping data on such traffic through its tunnels around Manhattan, and it was interested in having the problem studied. They have an operations research group, headed by Mr. Leslie E. Edie, which has worked closely with the M.I.T. Operations Research Center, providing us with data, so our simulations could be realistic.

The simulation was not simple. Each driver was given a maximum speed at which he would run, was given a reaction time, and was programmed to accelerate and decelerate according to the relative speed and distance between his car and the car ahead, with parameters which varied from car to car. The statistical distribution of these parameters was, in part, obtained from data collected by the General Motors operations research team and, in part, had to be determined from the simulation itself. By the time we had completed our first program, we had so many parameters and so much variability that the 704 ran only about five times as fast as the traffic itself. Also our simulation produced many more rear-end collisions than actually occur in traffic tunnels. But these first simulations showed us how to improve our program, what parts of the calculations could be simplified, what parameters needed to be modified, so that eventually the simulation ran much more rapidly than at first. Its dynamic behavior also corresponded closely to the Port Authority's measurements, the shock waves generated in dense traffic by any irregularity travelled back along the stream with a speed which depended on traffic flow in the correct manner, and the fluctuations in inter-car spacing were about the right size. Some of these dynamic properties turned out to be quite sensitive to some of the parameters in our model of the driver-car unit, and we believe the procedure of adjusting their value so that the simulation corresponded to observed behavior has obtained a quite accurate specification of driver-car behavior, more accurate than has been yet achieved by more direct measurements.

Once we had a program which simulated known traffic behavior, we were in a position to experiment with the system in a way one cannot do with actual traffic. We could trace out the effect of a "drunk driver", one having an abnormally long delay time, for example—and investigate the effect of speed limits and limits on inter-car spacing on the number of accidents and on the "through-put", the mean rate of flow of cars

through the tunnel. We were also in a position to investigate the cur-
ious "bottleneck" which occurs at the junction between the level part
of the tunnel and the upgrade whenever the traffic density gets large
enough. This grade is not enough to slow down a car, so it is at first
difficult to see why any bottleneck should occur there, and, indeed,
no mathematical model or simulation program which leaves out density
fluctuations can reproduce this effect.

When the density is large there is always a certain amount of
"spacing noise"; someone slows down a little, for some reason or
other, and this change produces a small shock wave of deceleration-
acceleration in the cars behind. But on the upgrade some of the cars
can't accelerate as fast, so that large spaces are present here, the
level region becomes correspondingly congested and the through-put
drops . Our simulation correctly reproduced this effect. The next
question was, could we find a way to minimize the effect? To make
a long story short, we were able to find a remedy and check it out on
the simulation. The trick is to interrupt the flow every so many cars,
to send the traffic through in "platoons" so as to break the shock waves
travelling back from the upgrade, so that the mean density on the level
is not more than that on the upgrade. If the platoon size and the inter-
platoon distance is chosen correctly, it is possible to obtain more
through-put than if the cars are allowed to crowd in as fast as they
come. When this was tried on actual tunnel traffic by the Port Authority, about five percent more cars got through each hour than were able
to get through without "platooning".

In this second example the simulation actually enabled us to
work out details of the operation which were very difficult to measure
directly, and experiments with the simulation gave us enough clearer
insight into the overall behavior so we could suggest improvements in
the operating rules. We hope that further experiments will suggest an
appropriate analytic model which will correspond to the actual operation much more closely than any heretofore proposed. If we do succeed,
we will consider our simulations to have paid off handsomely.

One final example of simulation, one still more complicated, is
one started at the M.I.T. Computation Center by an inter-college team.
Professor Guy Orcutt, at that time in the Economics Department at
Harvard, Dr. Martin Greenberger of the M.I.T. School of Industrial
Management, and Dr. Korbel, then with the M.I.T. Computation Center
(Prof. Orcutt and Dr. Korbel are now here at the University of Wisconsin), set up a machine simulation of the economic behavior of a town,
as part of their program of economic forecasting. A few general remarks
may indicate the nature of the problem.

Every ten years the U. S. census gives an instantaneous snapshot of the economic status of the nation: how many people have married, what family incomes are, what jobs they have, and so on. After
another ten years we have another snapshot, but there is no detailed
correlation between the pictures. If we are to forecast accurately, we
should be able to follow individuals through the ten-year period, follow
their marriages, deaths, changes of jobs, and their economic

interactions; we should follow the details continuously through time.

It is manifestly impractical actually to observe enough people continuously, but it should be possible to set up a machine simulation, which can be adjusted so that it corresponds to the gross changes measured by the consecutive census figures. As with the previous example, one can use the simulation to check out the parameters. In the present example, the number of parameters was much larger, so the task was more difficult.

A typical group of 2,000 persons was chosen, appropriately distributed in age, marital and economic status to simulate census data for a town. Each of these persons was then checked each month, a Monte Carlo process was used to determine whether he got a raise, whether he married or bought a car or refrigerator or house, his status was accordingly modified and the effect of this change on others was taken into account. The probabilities that these various changes come about are to some extent known, some of the parameters had to be guessed at and the values adjusted later so that the end of the ten-year run would correspond with the next census figures. As you can perhaps appreciate, the program was immensely complex, but with clever programming it was gotten on the 704. Each ten-year's history took about ten hours of machine time. This is a lot of time on a big machine, but we feel the results are worth it.

Enough runs were made to determine the probabilities reasonably well and to check the stability of the simulation. When enough individuals are included in the simulation, you approximate a statistical universe, and the differences between duplicate runs are not large. A relatively small number of runs should thus provide a fairly good forecast. The runs taken last summer are being worked up. A detailed report should be available soon.

This concludes my discussion of examples of machine simulation of complex operations. We feel that their most promising use is as a substitute for operational experiments, that they should be used to gain deeper insight into the behavior of the operation so that, hopefully, an analytic model can be developed, which then can be used for prediction. We believe that the use of simulation as a surrogate experiment is more profitable than is its use as a computation technique, as is implied in the words Monte Carlo.

NOTES

*For a more detailed discussion of these problems, see "Notes on Operations Research, 1959", Technology Press, Cambridge, Mass.

Discussion of Paper Five

Dr. Howes: Before I ask my question, I would like to make a remark or two. I was glad to hear the reference in the discussion several times to Monte Carlo methods because, by and large, Monte Carlo seemed to be the only technique mentioned in your talk that offers a separate channel of verification of the type of conclusions that you might be coming up with as a result of theoretical studies. One might feel open to the charge of being a modern fortune teller or a modern swami if one were to believe such an analysis. Theoretical results should have some sort of second checking. I also noticed there was little reference to statistics. I can imagine an operations research group in which a large proportion of the people were doing nothing else but statistical analysis of the data that, providing something stronger and more worthwhile for its value than anything that could possibly be postulated on the basis of theory.

I am reminded of engineers who were called in to determine why the Tay Bridge fell in, and they found out that it couldn't have; therefore it didn't! I would like to mention, in addition to the techniques you had time to mention, many others that are in constant use in operations research offices which tend to give greater assurance to the results: statistical analysis, especially multiple regression analysis, wherever possible. In the case like the one you mentioned last, autocovariance analysis.

Further, after one has worked out a suitable solution by these methods of finite mathematics that you mentioned, the serious question that arises is how will the parameters that are postulated be manifested as statistical variables from the data when it is eventually observed. I think that detailed attention should be given to how the problem is to be eventually verified, even if it is impossible to carry out the verification. A study of the sampling distribution of the parameters would often be an important part of the operations research analysis.

I've heard a lot of disagreement as to what operations research actually consists of. I've heard two definitions. One is that operations research is the team approach... anybody can play... bringing together mathematicians, statisticians, actuaries, chemists, physicists, engineers of all kinds, and get them together and take what each of them has to contribute. On the other hand, I hear people who say there are certain specific techniques like linear programming, techniques of finite mathematics, that are specially useful in the field

79

of operations research. I would be interested in hearing your comment on what you think.

Dr. Morse: Let me comment on your first comments. Since this Conference is a discussion of applied mathematics, I did not discuss the immensely important role of experiment in operations research. You are quite right—the getting of experimental data is at least half of the whole job. In point of actual time, it is probably much more than that. In this respect, it is very much like all the other disciplines we've heard about and talked about today, where one has to do a great deal of hard experimental and observational work to get the equations which were talked about here. I agree with you on that.

There are a number of definitions of operations research. I have found that to make the definition too general leads one into all sorts of pitfalls. I myself prefer to say, as you noticed, that operations research is a study of operations. One must then define operations, as I did, and to point out that they can be studied experimentally and theoretically. It seems to me that this avoids a great number of pitfalls of trying to claim more than operations research does. Operations are not all of social activity by any means, but they are a fairly important branch of group activities. They are by nature rather closer to the sort of things that physical science deals with. Therefore, it makes more sense to apply mathematics AND quantitative experimental techniques to these phenomena. That is the reason that I prefer that kind of definition.

Dr. Rosen: I have a question on the use of simulation and Monte Carlo. One of the big difficulties with this, as I'm sure you know, is when to quit. You simulate the thing, and you run a number of cases, and the question is: does this represent the model and if so, how well? What sort of tricks or methods do you use?

Dr. Morse: I'm afraid we have been very simple-minded about these things. On very complicated systems we never get enough runs to get a staisfactorily statistical behavior. This is why I feel the approach, considering the experiment, is to me quite suggestive. A physicist can never experiment enough either, but he uses all the tricks and ideas that he has to cross-check the readings and to use what statistics he can, and so on, to give him a feeling for the solidity of his results. In many cases he doesn't use the most high-powered statistics. I'm not sure that this is a disadvantage. Perhaps making a few more runs on the experiment, with different settings, might be much better than trying a few more chi squared tests. The experimenter uses his intelligence and all the tricks he has learned to get the most data out of the fewest experiments. If you think of the simulation as an experiment once removed, and therefore a little more dangerous and therefore requiring more cross-checking with the original data, then to physical scientists this illuminates a great deal.

That is about all I can say in general. Every one of these simulations has its own little problems of checking, just as every physical experiment has its own little problem.

Dr. Fend: In regard to your third problem involving the census picture, I had the impression that there are quite a few parameters such as probability of marriage, babies, etc., which had to be fit in order to make the two pictures agree. Now, there's really no good way that I know of to make sure that you have a unique solution for them. Do you have any fancy way of testing it to be sure your solution is correct?

Dr. Morse: Do you want to say anything about this, Professor Orcutt, or is it too early? Perhaps I can say that Professor Orcutt and his helpers are engaged in writing up their most recent runs at MIT which will be out, I guess, next Spring. The details of their worries (and they've done a great deal of worrying about this, I'm sure) will be there. I'm sure they won't say they've got the final answer on it by any means. It's too big a job for that, but it seems to me a very promising way of looking at this whole problem.

Dr. Fend: Can you just tell me—is it possible to examine the evidence internally, or do you have to perform other experiments on the raw material in order to get the results out?

Dr. Orcutt: I don't know whether I can adequately deal with that right now. The basic relationships that are in the model are based upon data that were derived from various kinds of surveys. Thus, for example, sample survey data and census data were used as a basis for testing hypotheses about birth and marriage. So, in a sense, I would say that most of the testing was done before the pieces were assembled into the model. Now, then, after they are assembled and after you make runs, you can do a certain amount of testing at a more aggregated level that isn't possible until you have a model. That is, while you don't have the complete census every month, you do have the time series with aggregate number of births, marriages, and deaths which the series generated by the model should correspond to. I don't know if that is an adequate explanation or a statement of what was done, but in any case, the testing was done mostly before the model was built. Having gotten a model, additional testing may be done at various aggregative levels.

Dr. Fend: Then you use supplementary information? You cannot simply use the ten-year census?

Dr. Orcutt: We actually use a great deal of supplementary information.

Dr. Kimes: It appears to me there is a problem which you might call "feed back" involved here in connection with the economic conditions that determine how this population behaves...how they plan their family, how they plan their purchases, etc.; for their behavior will itself have an effect on the economic conditions. Take for example the case of a depression. The occurrence of a depression would affect the behavior of the population. On the other hand, their behavior could bring about a depression. Do you, then, simply assume that there will be a certain cycle of economic conditions that will determine their behavior, or do you take into account the fact that their behavior will affect these conditions, so that we have interacting events?

Dr. Orcutt: In what we did so far, we were taking the economic conditions, you might say the boundary conditions, as given. We had aggregative information about economic variables and this may be fed in as simulations are carried out. What we are shooting for is a much more grandiose thing in which you have not only households, but firms, governments, financial institutions, and so on, interacting. In this case that was was formerly taken as being given would then be generated and interaction would take place during every state of a simulation.

Dr. Morse: As in any of the operations research problems, one starts at the unit operational level and then tries to build things to-gether so that one can understand the larger and larger aggregates. As Professor Orcutt pointed out, as you begin to get these larger ag-gregates. As Professor Orcutt pointed out, as you begin to get these larger aggregates, the interaction from one to the other becomes more and more important. These are aspects that one runs into all the time.

Dr. Howes: Just one remark not on population, but an earlier item. Though Monte Carlo would be crude as compared with a theoretical solution, if I had started a Monte Carlo, I would certainly continue with it as long as there was any disagreement between it and the theory, because as long as any substantial discrepancy existed, I would be inclined to believe Monte Carlo before the theory.

Paper Six | **JOSEPH O. HIRSCHFELDER**

Mathematical Bottlenecks
in Theoretical Chemistry

There are two kinds of theoretical developments in chemistry—
the empirical theories based on experience, and the theoretical treatments which are firmly tied to the fundamental laws of physics. The
empirical notions have developed by the Darwinian process of surviv-
al by comparison with three hundred years of detailed experimental
observations. On this account the empirical notions are often very
close to the truth. The application of theoretical physics to chemical
problems is comparatively recent and because of the complexity of the
chemical problems it is fraught with mathematical difficulties. The
goal of theoretical chemistry is to explain the empirical rules for chemical behavior in usual situations and make reliable predictions for
chemical behavior under extreme conditions of temperature, pressure,
ionization, etc. where little experimental data exist.

In 1930, Dirac stated that all of the basic physical laws, which
are required for the solution of all chemical problems, are now known.
In a very real sense this is true since chemistry depends upon (1) quantum mechanics, (2) statistical mechanics, and (3) electricity and mag-
netism. Except for a very few problems in radio-chemistry and a few
extraordinarily sensitive problems in nuclear magnetic resonance, the
velocity of the particles in chemical problems is sufficiently small
compared to the velocity of light that all relativistic corrections can
be neglected. Thus, the further development of the unified field theory is not required for the solution of chemical problems.

At the present time we can write the basic equations and boundary
conditions which determine the chemical and physical properties of
matter. Generally these relations are of such a difficult mathematical
nature that we do not know any method for obtaining exact solutions.
Often we do not know , even in principle, of any method for successively approximating the solutions. Indeed, it is only in the very
small class of problems for which we possess satisfactory mathematical methods for approximating the solutions that high speed computing
devices are useful. Our emphasis in the field of theoretical chemistry

during the next few years should be in the development of new methods of solution so that a wider class of problems may become suitable
for solution by high speed computing machines.

We think of high speed computing as mathematical experimentation since it provides exactly the same sort of data as does laboratory
experimentation. We feed a set of assumed conditions and relationships into the computing machine and obtain a numerical answer. In
using numerical methods we have lost the functional relationships
which are necessary for a clear understanding of the nature of the solution. If the problem contains only one or two parameters, it is feasible to repeat the computations many times to map the answer as a
function of the parameters. However, in most physical or chemical
problems there are a great many parameters so that such a mapping may
not be feasible with even the highest speed machines. Thus, high
speed computation will never replace the need for theoretical solutions.
Indeed, as high speed computation becomes more generally used, it
will become increasingly important to develop simplified theoretical
treatments which couple the starting conditions and the answers in
such a simple manner as to provide us with an intuitive understanding.
Since these simplified theoretical treatments cannot be rigorous, it will
usually be necessary to adjust the numerical constants in the formulae
so as to agree with the results of the high speed computing. Thus, we
must regard semi-empirical theoretical treatments as a necessary ad-
junct to the high speed computations in the understanding of the solution of a complicated problem.

There is a great variety of theoretical chemical problems, but they
may be divided into a number of classes depending upon whether the
viewpoint is microscopic or macroscopic and whether the problem is
time-dependent or steady-state. Some problems are concerned with
the properties of matter; other problems deal with the emission and absorption of radiation; while still other problems (such as chemical kinetics) involve the cross-sections for disruptive collisions between
molecules.

Since we cannot hope to be encyclopedic in the short time available, I shall limit the discussion to a few of the key mathematical
problems which block the further development in rather large areas of
research. These are three rather fundamental mathematical bottlenecks.

I. Our inability to obtain satisfactory approximate solutions to the

Schrödinger equation for molecules or systems of molecules.

We do not possess any mathematical methods for calculating the
energy of interaction of atoms or molecules to the accuracy required
for practical purposes. Furthermore, we do not possess any mathematical method for determining the physical properties of molecular systems without first solving the energy problem in order to determine the
wave function.

If the variables were separable or the perturbations were really small, there would be no problem. Unfortunately, neither condition applies.

In 1934, Eisenhart showed that there are only eleven types of possible coordinate systems in which the Schrödinger equation is separable and these are characterized by coordinates which are confocal quadrics. It would seem very desirable to generalize the concept of separability so as to include the possibility of writing the wave function as a product of a kernel times the separable function. The kernel could be a predetermined function of all of the coordinates, and for each functional form of the kernel there would be different criteria for separability. In thinking of our molecular quantum mechanical problems it would seem necessary for the kernel to be the asymptotic solution of the wave function in the field of all of the singular points. At the present time it is even difficult to determine the asymptotic solution of the wave functions in a field of more than two singular points. Research along these lines might be very fruitful.

Calculations of energy for the past twenty years have made use of the Rayleigh-Ritz variational principle whereby the expectation value of the Hamiltonian using an approximate wave function is greater than the energy of the ground state of the system. The approximate wave functions are taken to be arbitrary linear combinations of a set of assumed functions and the variational principle is used to select the best linear combination. In this manner, twenty-four years ago, James and Coolidge varied thirteen parameters to determine the energy of formation of the hydrogen molecule to a precision comparable with experimental observations. This technique is readily adaptable to high speed computing machines and a great many scientists are now coding up their machines to solve any one of a few simple problems with very high precision. For example, last year Pekeris used a wave function with 1078 terms to solve the Schrödinger equation for the helium atom to obtain the energy of formation of the ground state of helium to eight place accuracy. In molecular problems, considerable ingenuity is being used in the computation of the difficult exchange integrals which are encountered. The complexity of the functional form of the approximate wave functions which are assumed is mainly limited by the difficulty of evaluating these exchange integrals.

Up to the present time, the Rayleigh-Ritz variational method has been used to determine the binding energy of a considerable number of diatomic molecules and a few triatomic molecules. Besides the difficulty of evaluating the exchange integrals, there is the problem of the very great precision which is required in the calculation of the energies of formation in order to obtain the binding energies to a precision of one percent (required for practical utilization). The trouble is that the binding energy is usually the small difference between two very large numbers, the energy of formation of the molecule and the energy of formation of the separated fragments. For example, the energy of formation of the chlorine molecule, Cl_2 , from its electrons and nuclei is approximately 25000 e.v. whereas the energy of binding of the two chlorine atoms is only 2 e.v. In order to calculate the binding energy of the two chlorine atoms to a precision of one percent, it would be necessary to calculate the energy of formation of the chlorine molecule to a precision of one part in 10^6 . Around 1935, James and Coolidge tried to calculate this binding energy and obtained a negative value, which means that their calculational errors were larger than the quantity which they were attempting to calculate. Even with the availability of high speed computing machines, such a calculation does not seem possible at the present time. At the present time most experts believe that unless we drastically improve our computational techniques it will never be possible to calculate the binding energy of diatomic molecules where the atoms are past the first row in the periodic table.

For exactly the same reason, it is extraordinarily difficult to calculate the energy of interaction between two molecules. As a matter of fact no one has succeeded in calculating an intermolecular potential energy curve with accuracy comparable to that which is obtained from experimental observations. In the case of the interaction of two helium atoms a precision of one part in 10^7 in the calculation of the energy of formation of the system is required in order to give the energy of interaction to a precision of one percent.

According to Coulson, quantum mechanicians can be divided into the two classes: A and B. The A class try to obtain rigorous solutions to the Schrödinger equations. Their problems are now limited to the small molecules. In addition, there are the B class quantum mechanicians who treat big molecules by empirically adjusting constants and arbitrarily setting equal to zero integrals which are difficult to evaluate. The class B quantum mechanicians are remarkably successful in predicting the binding energy, structure, and spectra of complex molecules. A large volume of computational work along these lines is being carried out both in the industrial laboratories and in the universities. I understand that du Pont is spending more than $2,000,000 a year for such calculations. In effect, class B quantum mechanics transcribes all of the art and know-how of organic chemistry into mathematical language. The big plum in quantum mechanical research will go to the person who can explain the class B procedures in terms of mathematically justifiable approximations to the solutions of the Schrödinger equations. If there were only one system of type B calculations, one would have some sort of basis for the start of an investigation. However, there are two completely different types of class B calculations both of which give comparable agreement with experiments. In the MO-LCAO (molecular-orbital linear-combination-of-atomic-orbitals) scheme, the exchange integrals are assigned empirical values and all of the binding energy is ascribed to the potential energy of the system. Whereas, in the FE-MO (free-electron molecular-orbital) scheme, it is only the kinetic energy which determines the binding energy. Of course, neither scheme could possibly be right, since the virial theorem establishes a simple relation between the potential and kinetic energy of the molecule. Thus, we seek a third, and perhaps quite different, approach which will lead to substantially the same results as the other two for the stable ground state molecules which are presently studied.

There are many molecular quantum mechanical problems where even qualitative results have great practical importance. For example, in the upper atmosphere, between 30 and 50 kilometers, we know that there is a rather large percentage of ozone in the air. We have many reasons to suppose that in this same region there must be equally large concentrations of the molecule O_2H . This species is known to exist in large quantities in flames and has been verified in a mass spectrograph. However, O_2H has not been identified at the present time by spectroscopic means. If only the quantum mechanicians of either the A or B class could estimate the electronic and vibrational frequencies to be expected for this molecule, the experimentalists would probably find it easy to assign particular band structures to this species.

The problem of determining binding energies represents an interesting type of problem. When two atoms or two molecular fragments interact, it is only the orbitals of the outermost electrons which are appreciably perturbed. Whereas the energy of formation of molecules is proportional to the expectation value of $1/r$, and hence is determined principally by the electron distribution close to the nuclei. In contrast, the binding energy depends more closely on the expectation value of r^2 and is determined principally by the outermost portions of the charge distribution. Thus, charge distributions which give good value for the energy of formation may not be sufficiently accurate to be useful in determining binding energies.

Attempts have been made to use perturbation methods to calculate the binding energies. However, most perturbation methods require knowledge of the complete sets of wave functions for the separated molecular fragments and this is never available except in the case of hydrogen atoms. In most cases, there is a large contribution from the continuum states which are very difficult to treat. And then, most perturbation treatments are only asymptotically convergent, providing a satisfactory solution for extremely large separations, but failing completely at slightly smaller separations.

Thus we should seek a new type of variational principle which will assign much greater importance to the outermost portions of the charge distributions. Clearly, for every differential equation of the Schrödinger type, there must exist an infinite number of variational principles. Perhaps one of these will provide the answer to our problem.

One radically new approach to molecular quantum mechanics is the formulation in terms of density matrices. Instead of dealing with wave functions in 3N variables for an N particle system, it is possible to express the expectation values for all physical properties in terms of the twelve variable generalized density matrix

$$\Gamma(\underline{r}'_1, \underline{r}'_2 | \underline{r}_1, \underline{r}_2) = \frac{N(N-1)}{2} \int \cdots \int \Psi^*(\underline{r}'_1, \underline{r}'_2, \underline{r}_3, \cdots \underline{r}_N) \, \Psi(\underline{r}_1, \underline{r}_2, \underline{r}_3, \cdots \underline{r}_N)$$

$$dr_3 \cdots dr_N \cdot (1)$$

Unfortunately it is very difficult to develop a variational principle for the direct determination of the generalized density matrix, since a given expression for the generalized density matrix may not be derivable from an acceptable functional form for the wave function. Working backwards from an arbitrary expression for $\Gamma(\underline{r}'_1, \underline{r}'_2; \underline{r}_1, \underline{r}_2)$ one frequently obtains expressions for $\Psi^*(\underline{r}_1, \underline{r}_2, \underline{r}_3, \cdots \underline{r}_N) \Psi(\underline{r}_1, \underline{r}_2, \underline{r}_3, \cdots \underline{r}_N)$ which are not real. At the present time there is a considerable number of top-flight quantum mechanicians who are trying to complete the generalized density matrix formation.

In the period from 1928 to 1933 there was a great interest among mathematicians in the development of quantum mechanics. We very much need their help at the present time.

II. Our inability to generalize the Boltzmann equation to give the set of distribution functions for dense gases in which the molecules possess internal degrees of freedom. [1]

Once we have learned how to solve the Schrödinger equation and determine the physical properties of individual molecules, we will still be faced with a very difficult set of statistical mechanical problems which correspond to generalizing the Boltzmann equation.

The macroscopic physical and chemical properties of a system can be expresed in terms of the hierarchy of distribution functions:

$$f_1(\underline{r}_1, \underline{v}_1; t; \underline{q}_1)$$
$$f_2(\underline{r}_1, \underline{v}_1; \underline{r}_2, \underline{v}_2; t; \underline{Q}, \underline{q}_1, \underline{q}_2)$$
$$f_3(\ldots \ldots \ldots \ldots \ldots)$$
$$\ldots \ldots \ldots \ldots \ldots \ldots)$$
$$f_N(\underline{r}_1, \underline{v}_1; \ldots; \underline{r}_N, \underline{v}_N; t; \underline{Q}, \underline{q}_1, \ldots, \underline{q}_N) \quad (2)$$

Here f_1 gives the number of molecules at time t which possess the quantum numbers $\underline{q}_1$, lie within a unit volume surrounding the point $\underline{r}_1$, and have a velocity which lies within a unit velocity volume of $\underline{v}_1$. The f_2 is the pair distribution function which tells the correlation of the position and velocity of molecular pairs "1" and "2". Here $\underline{q}_1$ and $\underline{q}_2$ are the quantum numbers for the separated molecules and $\underline{Q}$ is the set of quantum numbers for the combined double molecule. The f_3 is the distribution function for clusters of three molecules. The f_N is the distribution function for the full ensemble of N particles. The Liouville equation determines the behavior of f_N. In general an f_{n-1} is derivable from an f_n by performing integrations over one set of molecular coordinates. Thus the $f_1, f_2, f_3, \ldots$ are all determined by the f_N .

Kirkwood derived the equation of change of f_1 in terms of f_2, the equation of change of f_2 in terms of f_3 , etc. for a substance composed of molecules without internal degrees of freedom. In order to derive the Boltzmann equation for f_1 he found it necessary to introduce time-smoothing of the distribution function. Other people such as Grad do not believe this is necessary. In any case the range of applicability of the Boltzmann equation is not yet known.

Most of the physical and chemical properties of materials can be expressed in terms of only f_1 and f_2 . Furthermore, for the physical properties it is only the first three moments of f_1 which are important. These three moments determine the number density, pressure tensor, and local energy or temperature. Hilbert regarded as an interesting paradox the fact that the higher moments of f_1 do not seem to have any importance for determining the macroscopic properties of a gas. Gradually this paradox is being resolved. Recently Brout and Prigogine have shown that if f_N is taken to be an arbitrary function at time zero, then, after a time comparable with the time between molecular collisions, the resulting f_1 will become altered into a form which satisfies the Boltzmann equation. Furthermore, Grad has shown that if f_1 is taken to be an arbitrary function it will become changed in a time comparable with the time between collisions so that its higher moments agree with those obtained on the basis of the Chapman-Enskog approach. Thus, after a short time, the higher moments of f_1 are determined by the first three moments.

In order to treat dense gases, Kirkwood and others made the ad hoc closure assumption that f_3 is related to f_1 and f_2 by the "superposition principle". The intrinsic accuracy of the superposition principle is not yet known. However, the rigorous treatment of dense gases or condensed systems is extraordinarily difficult. In such systems it is no longer possible to deal in terms of trajectories which start and end with separated molecules, since the molecules spend most of their time in a state of collision. At the present time we do not even possess a satisfactory formulation for the steady state problem which leads to the equation of state of liquids or dense gases.

The present formulation of kinetic theory does not take into account the non-spherical shape of the molecules or their internal degrees of freedom. At the present time Curtiss is trying to extend the equations of change of f_1 , first to non-spherical rigid molecules, and then to real non-spherical molecules. This generalization of kinetic theory involves some very intriguing conceptual problems. A purely quantum statistical mechanical formulation would not involve conceptual difficulties, but the resulting equations would be hopelessly difficult to solve. Thus, it seems desirable to treat the translational and rotational degrees of freedom classically. This introduces the difficulties that we do not know precisely how to perform the averages over the relative phases of motion of the molecules as they

enter into a state of collision. That is, the precise formulation of
the quasi-ergodic hypothesis must be generalized to encompass the
motions of systems of molecules with internal degrees of freedom.

Once the basic statistical mechanics is known, the rigorous
equations of change of the distribution functions can be derived.
Then we can formulate procedures for solving these equations. Un-
doubtedly we can use a perturbation scheme based upon the Chapman-
Enskog method for solving the Boltzmann equation. At this point there
will be opportunities for rather large scale numerical calculations of
equations of state, heat transfer, viscosity, and diffusion.

It is interesting to note that the high speed computing machines
can perform useful mathematical experimentation even when the basic
theory is not known. For example, Wood has calculated the equation
of state of dense gases and liquids making use of a Monte Carlo procedure. He considers 108 hypothetical molecules placed in a cubical
cell and supposes that the molecules interact pairwise according to a
prescribed law of force. One molecule at a time attempts to make a
move. This move is automatically accepted if it results in a decrease
in the energy of the system. However, if the move results in an increase in the energy E , it is accepted with a probability equal to
the Boltzmann factor, $\exp(-\Delta E/kT)$. Thus the move is sometimes
accepted and sometimes rejected. By making use of periodic boundary
conditions, the small number of molecules considered behave as
though they were a part of an infinite ensemble. In order to arrive at
a satisfactory distribution of the molecules for a particular condition
of temperature and density, it is sometimes necessary to consider
100,000 moves. This requires a large amount of computing time on
even the fastest computing machines.

Calculations of the Wood type provide the theoreticians with
extremely valuable data. For example, Dahler and I numerically integrated the Kirkwood integral equation to obtain the optimum free-volume
type of equation of state for a liquid. Our numerical results did not
agree with the experimental data. Perhaps, we might have been inclined to ascribe the lack of agreement to three and four body forces
which we did not consider. However, Wood's Monte Carlo calculations agree with experiments and ours do not. Thus, we conclude that
our assumed law of force between the molecules is not to blame, but,
rather, the free volume approximation is not satisfactory.

Recently, Wood has considered the equation of state of a system
composed of rigid sphere molecules with no forces of attraction.
Strangely enough, he finds that there is a phase transition between a
crystalline and a gaseous phase. This result has been verified by Alder who used an entirely different high speed computing machine technique in which he actually followed the dynamical trajectories of a
small ensemble of molecules. Many thousands of hours of computing
time on IBM 704's have been consumed in the solution of this problem.

III. Our inability to formulate the rate of chemical reactions in a form
   suitable for obtaining practical solutions. [2]

   With the present interest in chemical reactions taking place in
detonations, in shock tubes, in molecular beams, and in the partially
ionized plasma of the upper air, it is clear that our concepts of chemical reaction rates must be generalized. Furthermore, it is important
that the theoretical chemist be able to calculate reaction rates under
these extraordinary conditions, since direct experimental data may be
either very difficult or impossible to obtain. Unfortunately the theory
has not yet progressed to the point where we can use high speed computing machines to good advantage. This is another example of the
necessity for developing the basic mathematical methods before large
scale numerical applications can be undertaken.
   The theoretical chemist must be able to cope with problems in
which the notion of local temperature may be ill-defined and the population of the various quantum states may bear no resemblance to a
Boltzmann distribution. Often he must consider simultaneously the
aerodynamical problems of heat transfer, viscosity, and diffusion, as
well as the purely chemical rate problems. In order to treat such problems it is necessary to consider chemical reactions on a purely collis-
ional basis. This requires some major advances in our ability to solve
both the quantum mechanics of the individual collision processes and
the statistical mechanics of expressing the reaction rates in terms of
the ensemble of possible collisions.
   Chemical reaction rates specify the probability for certain col-
lission processes which disrupt the molecular species of the colliding
molecules and lead to the formation of resultant molecules of different
species. A typical bimolecular chemical reaction would be

$$A + B \rightarrow C + D \ . \tag{3}$$

Here A and B are the initial molecules which collide, and C and
D are the product molecules which result. If n_A is the number of
molecules of A and n_B is the number of molecules of B in the con-
tainer, then the chemist writes the reaction rate equation

$$dn_A/dt = -k(T)n_A n_B \ . \tag{4}$$

Here $k(T)$ is called the reaction rate constant although it is actually
a function of the temperature T . In order to make a more detailed
formulation of the reaction rate problem we must recognize that the
individual molecules exist in a wide variety of quantum states and
these quantum states affect their chemical reactivity. Thus the over-
all reaction, Eq. (3), is the manifold of reactions

$$A_i + B_j \rightarrow C_k + D_\ell \ . \tag{5}$$

Here $\underline{i}$, $\underline{j}$, $\underline{k}$, and $\underline{\ell}$ represent the quantum states of their respective molecules. Corresponding to the detailed reaction of Eq. (5),
there is the reaction rate constant $k_{ij}^{k\ell}$ (T) and Eq. (4) can be rewritten
in the form

$$dn_A/dt = -\sum_{ij} \sum_{k\ell} k_{ij}^{k\ell} (T)\, n_{Ai} n_{Bj} \ . \tag{6}$$

Eq. (6) is a generalization of Eq. (4) which includes those cases
where the populations of the various quantum states are not in thermal
equilibrium.

It is easy to show that if E is the relative kinetic energy of the
two molecules as they enter into a collision; m_A and m_B are the
masses of A and B respectively; and $C_{ij}^{k\ell}$ (E) is the cross-section
(as a function of E) for collisions characterized by the reaction of
Eq. (5), then

$$k_{ij}^{k\ell} (T) = \left(\frac{m_A + m_B}{\pi\, m_A\, m_B}\right)^{\frac{1}{2}} \left(\frac{2}{kT}\right)^{\frac{3}{2}} \int_0^\infty E\, C_{ij}^{k\ell} (E)\, \exp(-E/kT)dE \ . \tag{7}$$

Or, making use of a Laplace transform, the collision cross-section
can be expressed in terms of the detailed reaction rate constant,

$$C_{ij}^{k\ell} (E) = \frac{-k}{2E} \left(\frac{\pi m_A\, m_B}{m_A + m_B}\right)^{\frac{1}{2}} \int_0^\infty (2kT)^{-\frac{1}{2}} k_{ij}^{k\ell} (T)\, \exp(-E/kT)dT \ . \tag{8}$$

Thus the calculation of the reaction rate constants as functions
of temperature can be reduced to the calculation of the collision cross-
sections as functions of relative kinetic energy. However, the cross-
sections can be expressed in terms of the differential scattering
cross-sections, $I_{ij}^{k\ell}$ (E, θ, φ) , which give the probability that such
a collision takes place. Here θ is defined as the angle between the
final trajectory of molecule C and the initial trajectory of molecule
A . The angle φ is defined as the angle between the plane including
the final trajectories of C and D and the plane including the initial
trajectories of A and B . Thus,

$$C_{ij}^{k\ell} (E) = \int_0^{2\pi} \int_0^{\pi} I_{ij}^{k\ell}(E, \theta, \phi)\sin\theta\, d\theta\, d\phi \ . \tag{9}$$

In molecular beam experiments, such as Taylor is performing at Oak
Ridge, the $I_{ij}^{k\ell}(E, \theta, \phi)$ are measured directly. The relations given by
Eqs. (7), (8), and (9) should be useful in comparing the results of mol-
ecular beam experiments with other types of reaction rate studies.

In order to make a priori theoretical calculations of reaction
rates, it is necessary to further decompose the differential scattering
cross-sections to indicate the set of quantum numbers Q of the double
molecule which occurs in the collision. The nature of the collision
process depends on the values of Q . Thus, if two hydrogen atoms
in their ground states collide, they may interact in the $^1\Sigma_g^+$ state

which has the potential energy curve of the normal hydrogen molecule, or they may interact in the $^3\sum_u^+$ state which has the purely repulsive potential energy curve of the first excited state of the hydrogen molecule. In this example, Q would represent either the $^1\sum_g^+$ or the $^3\sum_u^+$ quantum numbers. Let us designate the Q specified differential scattering cross sections by $I_{ij}^{k\ell}(E, \theta, \phi; \underline{Q})$. Then

$$I_{ij}^{k\ell}(E, \theta, \phi) = \sum_{\underline{Q}} W(\underline{i}, \underline{j}; \underline{Q}) \, I_{ij}^{k\ell}(E, \theta, \phi; \underline{Q}) \ . \quad (10)$$

Here $W(\underline{i}, \underline{j}; \underline{Q})$ is the a priori probability that states $\underline{i}$ and $\underline{j}$ of the separated molecules couple to form a double molecule in the state $\underline{Q}$. Generally $W(\underline{i}, \underline{j}; \underline{Q})$ is the ratio of the statistical degeneracy of the state $\underline{Q}$ to the sum of the statistical degeneracies of all of the accessible double molecule states. Thus, in our example, the probability of the two hydrogen atoms combining to form the $^1\sum_g^+$ is 1/4.

For a purely quantum mechanical calculation of reaction rates one would attempt to calculate the differential scattering cross-sections directly. However, such a calculation would seem hopelessly difficult. Furthermore, even at room temperature one would have to make separate calculations for each of a tremendous number of translational and rotational quantum states. Thus, it appears more sensible to treat the relative translational and rotational motions of the molecules classically and the vibrational and electronic motions quantum mechanically. In this case one can define the impact parameter b (which is the miss distance if the collision took place with a straight line relative trajectory corresponding to no intermolecular forces) and the azimuthal angle ϵ (describing the orientation of the plane of the initial relative motion). Then one can introduce a new function $P_{ij}^{k\ell}(E, \theta, \phi; \underline{Q}; b, \epsilon)$ such that

$$I_{ij}^{k\ell}(E, \theta, \phi; \underline{Q}) = \int_0^{2\pi} \int_0^\infty P_{ij}^{k\ell}(E, \theta, \phi; \underline{Q}; b, \epsilon) b \, db \, d\epsilon \ . \quad (11)$$

Indeed the calculation of the $P_{ij}^{k\ell}(E, \theta, \phi; \underline{Q}; b, \epsilon)$ is the objective of any purely theoretical treatment of chemical reaction rates. In principle one might be able to make such a calculation on a rigorous basis. However, in practice it is much simpler to invoke the Born-Oppenheimer separation between the electronic and nuclear degrees of freedom. To do this, we hold the nuclei clamped in a fixed configuration and calculate the electronic energy of the system. The electronic energy then serves as the potential energy for the motion of the nuclei. For each set of double-molecule quantum numbers $\underline{Q}$ one obtains a separate potential energy surface. The $P_{ij}^{k\ell}(E, \theta, \phi; \underline{Q}; b, \epsilon)$ can then be calculated by following the classical motion on such a potential energy surface of a statistical ensemble of colliding molecules.

Unfortunately, at the present time our inability to obtain satisfactory solutions to the Schrödinger equation prevents us from

constructing realistic potential energy surfaces. However, because
of deviations from the Born-Oppenheimer separation, we do not know
whether such a treatment would give good values for the differential
scattering cross-sections. These deviations make the collisions non-
adiabatic in the Ehrenfest sense, so that the quantum numbers $\underline{Q}$
have a probability of changing during the course of a collision. If
the collisions are frequently non-adiabatic, then one must discard
the notion of intermolecular forces and potential energy surfaces and
treat the full quantum mechanical problem in which electronic and
nuclear motions are treated on the same basis. This corresponds to
making direct calculations of the $I_{jk}^{k\ell}$ (E, θ, ϕ) .

Because of the extraordinary difficulty of making rigorous
calculations of the reaction rates, Eyring has developed a very useful scheme for approximating these rates. He maps the collision trajectories on a potential energy surface. Most of the collisions
corresponding to chemical reactions come close to a saddle point
which he calls the activated state. Eyring then assumes that statistical equilibrium is maintained in the ensemble of molecular collisions
up to the vicinity of the activated state. In order to calculate reaction rates by this method, it is only necessary to know the potential
energy and its principal radii of curvature at the activated state. At
the present time there is no adequate experimental data to check the
accuracy of the Eyring calculations. The set of reactions:
$H + H_2$ (ortho) $\rightarrow H_2$ (para) $+ H$, $D + H_2 \rightarrow DH + H$, etc. should be
ideal for making such a comparison but, so far, the experimental re-
sults have not been sufficiently precise. Wall is using the ILLIAC
to calculate the trajectories of a set of collisions assuming a hypothetical potential energy surface. By calculating a sufficient number
of such trajectories he hopes to estimate the $P_{ij}^{k\ell}$ (E, θ, ϕ; $\underline{Q}$; b, ϵ) for
a hypothetical chemical reaction, and use Eqs. (11), (9), and (7) (in
that order) to calculate values of $k_{ij}^{k\ell}$ (T) which can be compared
with Eyring type reaction rates.

It appears likely that during the next twenty years the rigorous
calculations of chemical reaction rates will become feasible. When
this happens, mathematical experimentation will serve as a valuable
supplement to the experimentation in the laboratory.

In conclusion I want to emphasize that I have confined my discussion to the mathematical bottlenecks in theoretical chemistry. I
have not mentioned the wide variety of practical problems that we
know how to solve by computational means. I could have told you
about the very large scale computational program at the National Bureau of Standards to determine the thermodynamical properties of
thousands of molecules over a wide range of temperature and pressure
from a knowledge of the spectroscopic energy levels. I could have
stressed the large scale computational programs at MIT, Cambridge,
Tokyo, Chicago, etc. to calculate the integrals required in the solution of molecular quantum mechanical problems. I could have discussed the use of high speed computing to unravel the structure of
proteins or the structure of new types of high polymers on the basis

of x-ray diffraction measurements. There are indeed a wide variety of chemical problems for which high speed computing is extremely valuable.

As new mathematical models are developed for the formulation and solution of the basic problems of theoretical chemistry, the opportunities for useful high speed computations will increase without limit.

REFERENCES

1. C. F. Curtiss, "Annual Review of Physical Chemistry", 9, 379 (1958).

2. M. A. Eliason and J. O. Hirschfelder, J. Chem. Phys. 30, 1426 (1959).

The background for most of this discussion is given in "Molecular Theory of Gases and Liquids" (John Wiley, 1955) by J. O. Hirschfelder, C. F. Curtiss, and R. B. Bird.

Discussion of Paper Six

Dr. Young: Concerning the generalizations of the methods of separation of variables, I would like to call attention to a work of Professor M. H. Martin of the University of Maryland. He considers finite sums of products of functions of x times functions of y . No one of these products satisfies the differential equation, but the finite sum does satisfy the differential equation.

Dr. Hirschfelder: That is the approach of this natural spin orbital method.

Dr. Henrici: The possibility of representing the wave functions in the form $\psi(x, y) = K(x, y)f(x)g(y)$, where K is a function which depends only on the coordinate system, has been studied in a paper by N. Levinson and M. Redheffer (Quart. Appl. Math., 1948). The result is essentially negative: Such a representation is possible (with non-trivial K) only for the limiting case of the potential equation, and here only for one or two special coordinate systems.

Magnetohydrodynamics

Your announcement says that the speakers have been asked to set forth, as they see them, the mathematical problems that stand astride the advance of their specialties. To answer this question is to some extent to confess one's own ignorance, because the problems that stand in the way of one's work is a function of one's own competence, and so, to some extent, by trying to say what the mathematical problems are which stand astride progress, one may, in fact, be expressing one's own lack of knowledge of the relevant fields of mathematics.

I recall what Wallace Eckert, Director of the IBM Watson Laboratory at Columbia, once told me regarding his colleague, L. H. Thomas. L. H. Thomas, as you know, is a distinguished physicist; and apparently one of his duties in the Laboratory is to meet people of various sorts: physicists, chemists, and others who come to the Laboratory for assistance with problems believing that high speed computing is necessary for their solution. Apparently by the time these people had discussed their problems with L. H. Thomas, they had obtained from him analytical solutions to their problems; and, as Dr. Eckert added, Thomas was not proving too good an advertisement for the high speed computers!

So, it is to some extent a question as to how much one is acquainted with the large body of mathematical knowledge. Nevertheless, I think it is also true that the study of special branches of applied mathematics often leads to problems which could perhaps not have been anticipated otherwise.

I want to consider today a few typical problems which have arisen in some recent work, and which conceivably have some mathematical interest. I am not going to restrict my discussion specifically to hydromagnetics because, after all, hydromagnetics is to a very large extent an extension of hydrodynamics; and very often progress towards the solution of particular problems in hydromagnetics is stalled not because of the special difficulties of hydromagnetics, but because of the difficulties which already confront the solution of the hydrodynamical problem from which they are derived.

I shall consider problems which arise in three different connections.

I. Gravitational equilibrium of an incompressible fluid mass with axisymmetric fluid motions and magnetic fields

Axisymmetric fluid motions in an incompressible fluid can be specified in terms of two scalar functions, U and V (say). Similarly, axisymmetric magnetic fields can be specified in terms of two other scalar functions, P and T (say). If (ϖ, ϕ, z) define a cylindrical system of coordinates where z is along the axis of symmetry, then U , V , P , and T are functions of ϖ and z only. One finds that the equations of motion and of Maxwell reduce to the following set of equations:

$$\varpi^3 \frac{\partial P}{\partial t} = [\varpi^2 U, \varpi^2 P] , \tag{1}$$

$$\varpi \frac{\partial T}{\partial t} = [\varpi^2 U, T] + [V, \varpi^2 P] , \tag{2}$$

$$\varpi^3 \frac{\partial V}{\partial t} = [\varpi^2 T, \varpi^2 P] + [\varpi^2 U, \varpi^2 V] \tag{3}$$

and

$$\varpi \frac{\partial}{\partial t} \Delta_5 U = [\Delta_5 P, \varpi^2 P] - [\Delta_5 U, \varpi^2 U]$$
$$- [V, \varpi^2 V] - [\varpi^2 T, T] , \tag{4}$$

where
$$[\phi, \psi] = \frac{\partial \phi}{\partial z} \frac{\partial \psi}{\partial \varpi} - \frac{\partial \phi}{\partial \varpi} \frac{\partial \psi}{\partial z} , \tag{5}$$

and
$$\Delta_5 = \frac{\partial^2}{\partial \varpi^2} + \frac{3}{\varpi} \frac{\partial}{\partial \varpi} + \frac{\partial^2}{\partial z^2} . \tag{6}$$

Under conditions of equilibrium the left-hand sides of equations (1)-(4) vanish and it is remarkable that the equations can be solved, even though the solution is only a "formal" one. One finds, for example, from the first three equations that

$$\varpi^2 U = F(\varpi^2 P) \tag{7}$$

$$V = T F'(\varpi^2 P) + G(\varpi^2 P) , \tag{8}$$
and
$$\varpi^2 T = \varpi^2 V F'(\varpi^2 P) + N(\varpi^2 P) \tag{9}$$

where F , G , and N are arbitrary functions of $\varpi^2 P$ and the prime denotes differentiation with respect to the argument. Equation (4) then gives

$$\Delta_5 P = F'(\varpi^2 P)\Delta_5 U - \varpi^2 TVF''(\varpi^2 P) - \varpi^2 VG'(\varpi^2 P)$$

$$- TN'(\varpi^2 P) + M(\varpi^2 P) \tag{10}$$

where M is a further arbitrary function of $\varpi^2 P$.

The occurrence of so many arbitrary functions in equation (10) makes its usefulness very limited. However, the origin of the large degree of freedom which is apparent, appears to stem from the fact that for a closed system governed by equations (1)-(4) we have integrals of similar generality. Thus, one can show that the equations allow the following integrals:

$$I_1 = \int M^+(\varpi^2 P)d\tau , \tag{11}$$

$$I_2 = \int TN(\varpi^2 P)d\tau , \tag{12}$$

$$I_3 = \int \{F(\varpi^2 P)\Delta_5 U - \varpi^2 TVF'(\varpi^2 P)\}d\tau , \tag{13}$$

$$I_4 = \int \varpi^2 VG(\varpi^2 P)d\tau \tag{14}$$

and

$$2E = \int \varpi^3(-P\Delta_5 P + T^2 + V^2 - U\Delta_5 U)d\tau , \tag{15}$$

where M^+ , N , F and G are arbitrary functions of $\varpi^2 P$ and integrations are effected over the whole volume. The last of these is the energy integral. And it appears that the equations of equilibrium essentially represent the minimum of E compatible with the integrals $I_1, \ldots, I_4$ being kept constant. On this basis a variational method of solving the equations of equilibrium appears possible though the full relationship is not clear.

II. Variational formulation of non-self-adjoint characteristic value problems in high order differential equations

The stability of viscous flow between rotating cylinders leads to the following characteristic value problem. Solve

$$(D^2-a^2)^2 u = (1+\alpha z)v \tag{16}$$

$$(D^2-a^2)v = -Ta^2 u , \tag{17}$$

together with the boundary conditions

$$u = Du = v = 0 \text{ for } z = 0 \text{ and } 1 , \tag{18}$$

where a and α are real constants. In the practical context α can be negative and indeed less than -1 so that $(1+\alpha z)$ has a zero in the admissible range of z ; and T is the characteristic value parameter.

Some years ago I devised a method of solving the foregoing equations which has proved successful for carrying out the solution numerically. The method is the following: since v is to vanish at z = 0 and 1 , we expand v in a sine series:

$$v = \sum_m C_m \sin m \pi z . \tag{19}$$

We insert this expansion in equation (16) and solve the equation and arrange that the solution satisfies the remaining boundary conditions on u . We then insert in equation (17) the assumed expansion for v and the derived expansion for u and obtain a secular equation for T in the usual manner.

Recently P. H. Roberts has shown that the foregoing method has a variational basis and that this in part explains why the method has proved convergent in practice.

Consider the system

$$(D^2 - a^2)^2 \phi = \psi \tag{20}$$

and
$$(D^2 - a^2)\psi = -Ta^2(1+az)\phi , \tag{21}$$

together with the boundary conditions

$$\phi = D\phi = \psi = 0 \text{ for } z = 0 \text{ and } 1 . \tag{22}$$

It can be shown that the characteristic values of the systems (16) and (17) on the one hand and of (20) and (21) on the other are the same; and moreover, that if ϕ_j and u_i are the proper solutions belonging to different characteristic values, then

$$\int_0^1 [(D^2 - a^2)u_i][(D^2 - a^2)\phi_j]dz = 0 \quad (i \neq j) . \tag{23}$$

This dual relationship between the solutions of the two systems enables the formulation of a variational principle; and the "natural" way one would use it for practical solutions coincides with the method I have described! It is important to state that dual systems can be constructed in many ways and the whole question of the notion of adjointness requires a re-evaluation.

III. Linear formulation of non-linear characteristic value problems

The stability of inviscid Couette flow leads to the following problem: solve

$$\frac{1}{x}\frac{d}{dx}(xy) - \frac{2m\Omega}{\sigma x}y = \frac{1}{\sigma^2}(\frac{m^2}{x^2} + k^2)z , \tag{24}$$

$$[\sigma^2 - \Phi(x)]y = \frac{dz}{dx} + \frac{2m\,\Omega}{\sigma x}\,z \;,$$ (25)

together with the boundary conditions

$$y = 0 \quad \text{for } x = x_1 \text{ and } x_2 \;,$$ (26)

where k is a real constant, m is an integer (zero, positive or negative), $\Omega(x)$ is a specified bounded function of x ,

$$\sigma = n + m\Omega \;,$$ (27)

n is a constant (which can be complex), and

$$\Phi(x) = 2\frac{\Omega}{x}\frac{d}{dx}(x^2\Omega) \;.$$ (28)

As the problem arises in physics, it is a characteristic value problem
for n for a given real k and specified $\Omega(x)$; and the principal
question concerns the conditions on $\Omega(x)$ which will lead to real or
complex characteristic values for n . The characteristic value parameter occurs non-linearly in the problem. I should like to consider
whether the basic question cannot be answered by inverting the problem somewhat. Consider equations (24)-(26) as a characteristic value problem for k^2 for a given n . If n were real, it can show that
the characteristic value problem is self-adjoint and Hermitian. Further, the problem is equivalent to finding extremal values of k^2 given
by

$$-k^2 = \frac{\displaystyle\int_{x_1}^{x_2} x\{(\sigma^2 - \Phi)y^2 + \frac{1}{\sigma^2}\frac{m^2}{x^2}z^2\}dx}{\displaystyle\int_{x_1}^{x_2} dx\, x\, z^2/\sigma^2} \;,$$ (29)

with equation (25) considered as a subsidiary condition. If Φ should,
for example, be everywhere negative, then, clearly no real n can
lead to a positive k^2 ; therefore, under these circumstances, real k
must imply a complex n . The question whether the arguments can
be refined to show that n must be necessarily real if Φ is everywhere positive is an open but important one. The main point I wish
to emphasize here is that there are perhaps avenues of solving problems in which the characteristic value parameters occurs non-linearly,
by reformulating the problems linearly in terms of other parameters
which occur in the equations.

Discussion of Paper Seven

Dr. Mangasarian: Do you as yet have, or are you trying, to develop criteria for the ability to construct an adjoint system from one which is not adjoint?

Dr. Chandrasekhar: What I meant is that there are adjoint systems. There are a great many. Empirically we have found that certain systems work and certain systems don't in more practical solutions of the various forms and the mathematical problem which is suggested is the following:

One must try to understand the rationale behind some of these; and the application of these variation systems based upon adjoint systems, no matter how you construct them, form a solution of practical problems.

Dr. Mangasarian: Can you a priori tell whether you can construct such an adjoint system? For a third order differential operator can you construct such a system?

Dr. Chandrasekhar: We have found that for this particular problem which I wrote down, you can construct it, and you can indeed construct it in more than one way.

Dr. Mangasarian: Do you have a criterion for a general case?

Dr. Chandrasekhar: Well, the only thing is if you give me an equation, I will look at it for some time and say we can or can't.

Dr. Mangasarian: There are some problems which are not susceptible to such a procedure.

Dr. Chandrasekhar: ...It is entirely possible, but in general, if you look at many of these problems that come in, if one has sufficient experience, then one can look at them and see the proper things one ought to do to it to get adjoint systems.

Dr. Young: I would like to say just a few words about the solution by numerical techniques on high-speed computers of eigenvalue problems for ordinary differential equation systems. These problems may be linear or nonlinear in the eigenvalue itself as long as the differential equations are linear in the dependent variables. I think that both of the problems considered by the speaker fall in that category.

The method used is to solve a single nonlinear equation of the form $f(\lambda) = 0$ where f is a function which is not written down explititly, but which can be computed for any given value of λ, usually by solving 3 or 4 simultaneous initial value ordinary differential equations; and you can solve such initial value problems on high-speed computers very conveniently. The idea then is to guess the value of

λ , to solve these 3 or 4 simultaneous equations, and to evaluate $f(\lambda)$ in order to measure how well the boundary conditions are satisfied.

The method of David Muller at the University of Illinois then gives you a method for guessing the next value of λ . You continue this process, evaluating $f(\lambda)$, getting improved values of λ , and iterating until you get convergence. This method, which has been used in a number of fairly complicated problems, is described in many places, one of which is the paper by Conte and myself which appeared in the Proceedings of a Symposium held in January 1957 on "Digital Computing in the Aircraft Industry," jointly sponsored by I. B. M. and New York University.

Dr. Chandrasekhar: Thank you very much. May I just say in the same connection we have used some of these ideas in analytic procedures. For example, I wrote down an equation a little while ago where the boundary conditions corresponded to u and u' being at 0,1 . You can construct a complete set of problem functions which satisfy these four boundary conditions. We have in fact constructed them and then expanded u in terms of those functions and put it into v , and it gives you a very good value. Sometime some years ago I tried to solve the Taylor problem in a finite gap width, and the solution was in terms of fourth order equation, the solutions of which are expressible as linear combinations of Bessel functions, the four kinds with the vanishing functions and derivatives on both ends, etc.

I would say that the attitude one has to these problems can be of two kinds. One is: "I have a problem here and I have to find a certain parameter T in order to, say, point the gun in some direction", and then, of course, you see you are interested in the value of T . You don't care how you get it. Or, you can say: "I want to solve the problem in a way in which the construction of the solution becomes clear." Now, it is conceivable that the latter method and the former may not always coincide in your objectives. I don't say they are contradictory, but they neither coincide. For example, if one considers the stability of viscous flow on a channel, you get a problem very similar to the one I wrote down, but one finds in that particular instance that one simple function, one term function which you can write down, does give an extremely adequate solution to the problem because you solved certain systems of equations before, and you have an analytic function and your grasp of the physical problem is better on that account. At least, I think so.

It seems to me that in all these problems, there are perhaps two objectives. One, of course, is to get the answers. The other is to get the answers in a way in which the human mind can comprehend— not merely the computer.

Paper Eight | J. SMAGORINSKY

On the Application of Numerical Methods to the Solution of Systems of Partial Differential Equations Arising in Meteorology

I. The Evolution of Dynamic Meteorology

Since I do not think that one can adequately convey the problems of numerical analysis peculiar to meteorological applications without some perspective regarding the physical basis, I would like to begin with a historical development of our understanding of atmospheric processes.

There are many distinguished names that have played a vital role in laying the groundwork of our understanding of the atmosphere in terms of the fundamental physical laws.* One of course can go back to Euler who generalized the Newtonian laws of particle dynamics to apply to continuous media. However it was not until the latter half of the nineteenth century that active consideration of the Eulerian equations in terms of the atmosphere began. Helmholtz (1858) wrote the hydrodynamic equations relative to a rotating framework and derived a circulation theorem for incompressible homogeneous flows. He also showed (1888) some awareness of the role of density stratification in the instability of atmospheric disturbances, which Margules (1903) investigated further in terms of transformations of potential to kinetic energy.

Early this century V. Bjerknes (1901) derived his famous circulation theorem for a rotating stratified fluid which clarified the nature of energy transformations responsible for the genesis of atmospheric vortices and more than ever demonstrated the applicability of the Eulerian equations to the atmosphere. He, in fact, suggested (1904) the stepwise integration of these equations as an initial value problem for the prediction of atmospheric evolutions. However it was somewhat later that Richardson (1922) conceived his grandiose scheme for numerically integrating the Eulerian equations (modified only by the hydrostatic approximation to eliminate sound wave solutions) taken together with the first law of thermodynamics. This attempt proved to be abortive, not merely because human beings make inefficient computing machines

but also because atmospheric motions were not yet well enough understood. The latter to a large measure must be attributed to the fact that
the atmosphere was inadequately described by the meager observations
available at that time—particularly there was a complete lack of knowledge of the vertical structure. It is an excellent example of the pitfalls of theorizing in a vacuum. Richardson's apparent failure dis-
couraged many meteorologists from further consideration of directly
applying the dynamic equations. Fortunately this did not deter the
amplification of observational networks nor the further study of atmospheric dynamics by the available mathematical tools—namely the theory of linear partial differential equations.

A number of important properties of the large scale atmospheric
motions was becoming apparent. Because the angular particle velocity
relative to the earth is small compared to the angular velocity of the
earth's rotation[#] the large scale motions are quasi-horizontal, the
relative acceleration is small compared to pressure gradient force, and
the divergence of the motions in horizontal planes, D , is small compared to the vorticity about vertical axes, ζ .

That is

$$f > \mid \zeta \mid > \mid D \mid > \mid \frac{1}{p_0} \int_0^{p_0} D \, dp \mid \tag{1}$$

where f is the vertical component of the earth's vorticity (also called
the Coriolis parameter), p is the pressure and p_0 is its value at the
earth's surface. The four quantities in the inequalities have magnitudes
of 10^{-4}, 2×10^{-5} , 5×10^{-6}, and $10^{-6} \sec^{-1}$, respectively.

Since large horizontal divergence D is associated with large amplitude gravitational motions, the energy contained by the gravitation-
ally controlled modes is small compared with the total wave energy;
and the Coriolis force approximately balances the pressure gradient
force; i.e. the motion is quasi-geostrophic. In fact Jeffreys (1926)
pointed out that the angular momentum balance must in essence be accomplished by the quasi-horizontal large-scale cyclones and anticy-
clones. Based on these findings Rossby (1939) derived a law stating
that the vertically integrated motion of the atmosphere conserves its
vertical component of absolute vorticity. This is reminiscent of the
work of Helmholtz and implies no source of kinetic energy through con-
versions of potential energy. Only redistribution of kinetic energy is
permitted by simple translation or by transformation from one wave
number to another through non-linear interaction. For the moment, neglecting the latter process, Rossby was able to show by linear methods
that the phase velocity of long waves is dictated by the wave length, the
variation of the Coriolis parameter with latitude, and the speed of the ambient current. This did not as yet explain the magnitude of the characteristic wave length except that the latter must obviously in part be attribut-
able to the distribution of continents, which in the northern hemisphere
would excite east-west wave numbers 2 and 3. The quasi-baratropic character of the atmosphere had already been suggested by the fact that the development of extratropical cyclones is observed not to be a continuous
process but rather a sporadic one both in time as well as in space.

However, Rossby (1940) realized the importance of kinetic energy sources and derived a more general theorem permitting sources of vorticity.

In separate studies Charney (1947), Eady (1949), and Fjørtoft (1950), discovered an instability theory which accounted for the sporadic nature of the conversion from potential to kinetic energy. This criterion for baroclinic instability depends on the vorticity of the earth's rotation and its variation with latitude, the mean available potential energy (a measure of which is the north-south temperature gradient or the vertical shear of the east-west current) and finally the variation of temperature with height (which we call the static stability). The theory is deducible by linear methods and unlike barotropic instability, where kinetic energy is transferred between wave numbers, baroclinic instability results in the transformation of potential energy of the ambient flow to potential and kinetic energy of a small disturbance. This theory predicts a disturbance wave length of maximum instability and therefore of characteristic horizontal scale having wave number 5 or 6, which is in excellent agreement with observation. Furthermore, Kuo (1949) and later Fjørtoft (1953) showed that kinetic energy so produced is transformed barotropically into lower wave numbers, to increase the amplitude of the longer waves and ultimately the speed of the ambient current, as well as into shorter waves which ultimately dissipate the energy by molecular viscosity. This of course is an extension of the stability theory of Rayleigh (1913) and Lin (1945) to rotating systems— the effect of the variation of the Coriolis parameter is a stabilizing one.

Concomitant with these developments the first high speed digital computer, the ENIAC, had been constructed at the University of Pennsylvania in 1944 and a group was established at the Institute for Advanced Study under von Neumann to design and build the next generation computing machine. Von Neumann was well aware of the history of dynamic meteorology and had initiated a small group at the Institute to consider meteorological applications.

At the same time, Charney (1948) and Eliassen (1949) had more or less independently come to the conclusion that a system of equations analogous to those of Rossby could be devised for the purpose of predicting the large scale components of motion. As effectively Rossby had done, they showed explicitly that the geostrophic approximation consistently applied to the Eulerian equations would filter out the gravitational solutions a priori, and so avoid the difficulty which Richardson himself did not recognize.

At the Institute for Advanced Study, Charney and Eliassen (1949) constructed a linear one-dimensional barotropic model suitable for hand calculation under arbitrary initial conditions by Green's function techniques. Their results were quite encouraging and prompted the construction of a two-dimensional non-linear barotropic model (Charney, Fjørtoft and von Neumann, 1950) to be integrated on the ENIAC (since the IAS machine had still to be completed). The elliptic part of the problem, expressing the constraint of quasi-geostrophic balance, was solved by finite Fourier transform techniques. The results were astoundingly good but already indicated the crucial role played by observations in establishing the initial conditions. Nevertheless the human forecaster suffers from the same data deficiencies and the numerical integrations showed a skill in 24-hour predictions comparable to that of a reasonably competent forecaster. Of course there were serious discrepancies between the numerical forecasts and observations. There was then a concerted effort to diagnose the source of discrepancy—variously attributed to baroclinic processes, ageostrophic motions (i.e. the divergent gravitational components), mountains, viscous effects, and external potential energy sources such as latent heat of condensation and heat transfer. On the other hand there are some who felt that the barotropic model itself could be improved upon, especially the numerical techniques. As might be suspected there was some truth in all these speculations. These non-linear barotropic forecasts did have the effect of kindling an interest in the world-wide meteorological community to the extent that research nuclei in "numerical weather prediction" were spontaneously created in academic and government institutions of many nations.

On the contention that a provision for baroclinic instability was crucially lacking, Phillips (1951) constructed a 2-level model (thus adding a third dimension) within the framework of the geostrophic hydrodynamics. This was reasonable since baroclinic instability was discovered through a linear geostrophic analysis. His results and later results of an improved 2-level model constructed by Charney and Phillips (1953) predicted not only the vertically integrated motions (as observed approximately at the atmosphere's mass-midpoint at the 500 mb pressure level, lying roughly at 6 km altitude) but lower level motions which we are physically more aware of. The low level forecasts were of course an improvement since we did not have them at all before, but the 500 mb forecasts were on the whole no better than before. A 3-level model gave more resolution and diminished vertical truncation error, but the skill at 500 mb remained essentially the same. However, by 1953 the nature and quality of the results implied operational utility and the Weather Bureau, Air Force, and Navy established the Joint Numerical Weather Prediction Unit. This action in some measure implies the level of goodness as judged by operational agencies who have of necessity hard-boiled standards of quality.

An alternative to the geostrophic approximation was devised independently by Charney (1955) and Fjørtoft (unpublished). This was the quasi-nondivergent approximation which also had the property of filtering the gravitational components. Instead of a simple Poisson equation expressing the constraint of quasi-geostrophic equilibrium for barotropic flows, a Monge-Ampére equation in the stream function must be satisfied. In some respects the quasi-nondivergent approximation is a generalization of the geostrophic approximation for barotropic flows and the results are somewhat better. However a dubious increase of understanding was forthcoming at the cost of a considerable increase in mathematical complexity. It was also difficult to consistently apply the approximation to baroclinic flows.

With faster computing machines attention again turned to the quasi-static Eulerian equations. Since there is a delicate quasi-balance between the pressure gradient and Coriolis forces for large scale motions, slight inconsistencies in the initial conditions or in the numerical techniques for specifying the boundary conditions gives rise to spurious gravitational modes of large amplitude which obscure the large scale motions. In 1956 Eliassen published a report outlining a somewhat novel finite differencing scheme in which the variables were partitioned into alternating grids depending on how they arose in the linear terms of the system of equations. For the same amount of data, truncation error was reduced at the expense of more complex logic and of interpolations to form the non-linear terms. This scheme was in connection with a renewed proposal for the numerical integration of the Eulerian equations. Phillips (1959a) succeeded in integrating the Eulerian equations for barotropic flows using the Eliassen grid and I (1958) was able to integrate the baroclinic viscous equations. Early this year Hinkelmann (1959) also successfully integrated the baroclinic equations.

This resurgence was timely since some, including myself, feel that the geostrophic or nondivergent approximation is most valid for the long quasi-barotropic waves. Although these approximations are capable of accounting for the growth of baroclinic waves, which are shorter than the barotropic waves, the interaction of the small amplitude inertial-gravitational components gives rise to potential-kinetic energy transformations which are almost always out of timewise phase with the geostrophic transformations§ (Smagorinsky 1959a). It was Solberg (1936) and Høiland (1941) who, based on the stability analysis of Helmholtz (1888), demonstrated from the assumption of conservation of absolute momentum that instability is possible if the absolute vorticity in isentropic surfaces becomes negative. This latter process is possible only if gravitational solutions are admissible.

It is of interest to note the behavior of the quasi-geostrophic elliptic consistency condition for the vertical motion relative to pressure surfaces $\omega \equiv dp/dt$, where t is time (see for example Smagorinsky, 1956):

$$\nabla^2 H\omega - f(\zeta + f)\omega = W[\phi(x, y, p)] \tag{2}$$

Here

$$H \equiv \frac{\partial \phi}{\partial p} \frac{\partial \ln \theta}{\partial p} \tag{3}$$

is a measure of the static or buoyant stability and ϕ is geopotential. ∇^2 is the two-dimensional Laplace operator in the coordinates x, y which lie within the p-surfaces. θ is the potential temperature and is given by

$$\ln \theta = \text{constant} + \frac{c_v}{c_p} \ln p + \ln (-\frac{\partial \phi}{\partial p}) \tag{4}$$

in which c_v/c_p is the ratio of specific heats of air at constant volume and constant pressure. We assume that $H > 0$, i.e. only stable buoyancy oscillations are possible and hence the hydrostatic approximation is valid. We then note that (2) becomes hyperbolic when the absolute vorticity $\zeta + f < 0$, violating the filtering inequalities (1). Hence the mathematical formulation fails when the physical approximations are violated. This of course would not occur with the Eulerian equations.

II. Problems of Employing Numerical Techniques

A. Initial Data

The type of instrumentation operationally available in meteorology is generally dictated by the parameters which are measurable in the atmosphere. For instance at the ground one would measure the barometric pressure, temperature, the humidity and the wind velocity. Balloon carried instrumentation, of which the network is considerably less dense than for surface observations, is capable of measuring the temperature, humidity and wind velocity as a function of the barometric pressure. By means of the hydrostatic approximation and the pressure at the height above sea level.

In spite of the fact that much of the earth's surface is not covered by the existing observational network, especially over the oceans and the polar regions, it is well known that only a small fraction of the information content of the observations which we do have is extracted and utilized. This is probably connected with the fact that a human being can at best scan data simultaneously in only two dimensions. The vertical component of velocity of comparable scale to the measured horizontal component is unobservable and although in principle the divergence of the wind can be calculated as well as the geostrophic departure (since both the wind and pressure are observed independently), the error of measurement is of the same order as quantity itself so that even the sign is in question. The nature of the observables of the atmosphere leads to redundancies which have been used as a directive in constructing filtered models, i.e. the fact that large scale motions are empirically observed to be quasi-geostrophic and quasi-nondivergent has suggested employing these as dynamical approximations. Hence in preparing initial data for models based on geostrophic or nondivergence hydrodynamics, these unobservables do not raise a problem. In fact one can make use of the fact that the pressure and wind are to a very good approximation redundant in order to more firmly specify either the wind or pressure distribution in areas where the data density is sparse

What was an advantage in determining the initial conditions for the geostrophic equations turns out to be a still yet unresolvable difficulty for the Eulerian equations: these require the independent initial specification of the wind and pressure. It is precisely the small departure from redundancy, i.e. the degree to which this data is divergent and nongeostrophic, that gives a measure of the amplitude of the gravitational components in the initial data. Since these small quantities

are difficult to measure, small errors can give rise to spurious gravitational waves of high energy which can obscure the larger scale motions and do more damage than good. It has been proposed by Charney
(1955) and by Eliassen (1956) that the gravitational waves be completely eliminated from the initial data by requiring that the initial
winds satisfy the condition that the horizontal divergence vanish
identically. This in no way inhibits the excitation of gravitational
waves in the interior of time. However it has been found that such
an approximation destroys too much of the information content of the
initial data and therefore has a deleterious effect on the predictions.
It has been further suggested by Hinkelmann (1959) and by Phillips
(1959a) that one should permit that divergence which is necessary to
maintain quasi-geostrophic balance—with this weaker constraint some
improvement has been noted in the resulting integrations. However it
still appears that these approximations are too restrictive and it is
likely that less damaging means can be devised such that the gravitational modes are not eliminated from the initial data, but rather are
constrained weakly by controlling in the initial data the partitioning
of the rate of conversion of potential energy into the kinetic energy
of the divergent and rotational components (Smagorinsky, 1959b).

B. Time Integration

The method most often used for the time quadratures has been that
of explicit central differences with forward differences only used initially. Where explicit central time differences can lead to computational instability, such as in viscous terms, forward differences have
been employed or when the viscosity is linear implicit techniques have
proven useful. The computational stability criterion for explicit time
integration requires rather small time differences. As one includes
modes of motion which have large characteristic phase velocities, the
problem of economy of computing time becomes a factor, despite the
fact that computing machines are becoming faster. Some consideration
has been given to the use of implicit methods which, with everything
else being equal, can proceed stably with longer time differences.
Whereas this provides an immediate advantage for linear equations,
nonlinear equations require iterative techniques in order to proceed
implicitly (Knox, 1958). The relative efficiency of implicit and explicit techniques therefore hinges on the rate of convergence of the
iteration procedure versus the ratio of the time difference intervals
for the two techniques.

C. Lateral Boundary Conditions

It has been convenient in meteorological applications to permit
the lateral boundaries to be placed over limited areas of the earth's
surface such that flow can pass through them. The physical boundary
conditions for such open regions are not obvious and whereas some inconsistencies in geostrophic frameworks do not appear to do catastrophic damage, the Eulerian equations are quite sensitive (Platzman,

1958). If an integration domain can be taken large enough so that
closed boundaries may be specified fairly reasonably, no inherent
difficulty arises in specifying the physical conditions. However, depending on the form of the physical equations, computational boundary
conditions are often necessary. As it turns out these cannot be specified arbitrarily but rather are determined by requiring that the difference
equation and the physical boundary conditions together satisfy exact
integral conditions corresponding to the continuous equations (Smagorinsky, 1958). It is obvious that if the domain is extended to a
sphere the problem of boundary conditions vanishes entirely since one
may only require that cyclic continuity conditions are satisfied.

D. Vertical Boundary Conditions and Vertical Truncation Error

The correct boundary condition at the top of the atmosphere must
be that the individual derivative of pressure ω vanish as the pressure approaches zero. The correct boundary condition at the bottom
of the atmosphere is that the normal velocity component vanish. For
viscous flows one must in addition give the stress at the lower boundary. For quasi-hydrostatic motions, which is all that we have been
concerned with, it is quite convenient to replace the height as a vertical coordinate by the pressure (Eliassen, 1949). If the surface of
the earth were geoidal, then the local time derivation of barometric
pressure at this boundary is a measure of the vertically integrated
horizontal divergence. Physically this reflects the amplitude of
acoustic-gravitational waves of the external type which have extremely small amplitude as is attested by the fact that surface pressure
undergoes variations of less than 5 percent between extremes. This
is reflected in the last term of the inequality (1). Physically these
external waves are most important when excited by the very large
scale continental influences and their admissibility is quite likely
needed in order to explain the quasi-stationary character of the very
long waves in the atmosphere (Burger, 1958). When the lower boundary is not geoidal, by virtue of the large scale orographic masses,
the picture is more complicated since it becomes extremely inconven-
ient to deal with pressure coordinate surfaces which are intersected
by the mountains and so give rise to multipli-connected regions for
which boundary conditions must be specified. An interesting device
is to replace pressure as the vertical coordinate by the pressure normalized by the surface pressure (Phillips, 1957a). This ratio is 0 at
the top of the atmosphere and 1 at the surface of the earth, giving
somewhat distorted coordinate surfaces and a more complicated system of differential equations. The virtue of this device is that it is
somewhat easier to be physically consistent with the kinematics of a
corrugated lower boundary.

The addition of greater resolution in the vertical has generally not
given rise to severe problems, however attempts in 3-level models to
include the dynamical effects of variable static stability brought to
light potential difficulties due to very sensitive truncation error in

certain quantities. To calculate the static stability according to (3) and (4) from 3 levels of information, at which the geopotential is given, requires the use of all 3 degrees of freedom since the static stability is a function of the second and first derivative of the geopotential with respect to pressure. If one uses the normal techniques of linear differences to calculate the static stability from the geopotential corresponding to the"standard atmosphere," which is defined analytically, one calculates the static stability with not only the wrong sign but of the wrong order of magnitude (Smagorinsky, 1956). It would therefore appear that considerably greater resolution would be required in the vertical in order to calculate the static stability. However, it is already recognized that a tremendous amount of redundancy already exists in data fields from level to level. For instance the data at the 700 mb pressure level is extremely highly correlated with the data at 500 mb. What then is the explanation of this paradox?

As was the case in specifying initial conditions, the paradox exists because it is precisely the small deviation from redundancy that we wish to measure. One observes only relatively small variation of the static stability: that is the temperature tends to vary linearly with height, or logarithmically with respect to pressure. Upon using this as the local difference approximation instead of the fact that the geopotential varies linearly with pressure, no difficulty is encountered in calculating the static stability from 3 degrees of freedom. A smaller systematic error also arises in calculating the temperature itself by means of linear first order differences of the geopotential with respect to pressure. Obviously this, too, may be reduced to use of the same transcendental difference technique.

E. Mapping

It is desirable to work in the complete spherical domain not only to eliminate the problem of lateral boundary conditions as I indicated earlier, but it is also necessary for problems involving longer term evolutions where influences in far off regions cannot be ignored. Of course, the data problem becomes somewhat more acute since such a large portion of the earth is covered by water. However, it is reasonable to believe that for long term integrations the details of initial conditions become less important since the viscous forces dull the memory of the atmosphere. The question then remains as to what is the most convenient type of mapping to use. In all previous applications it proved convenient to conformally map on either a polar stereographic or Mercator projection depending on the particular region to be mapped. For the sphere a spherical polar coordinate system seems reasonable but the singularities at the pole give rise to problems which are not easily resolvable. It has been suggested (Phillips, 1957b) that a combination of Mercator projection in equatorial latitudes mutually interpolated with two polar stereographic projections would be satisfactory. This has numerous advantages as well as disadvantages and one can easily argue that if interpolations of this sort are to be done that two polar stereographic projections interpolated in the region about the equator is more desirable. Frankly I am not particularly happy with any of the possibilities which I have mentioned, although we ourselves are in the process of using the latter as an immediate expedient. Consideration so far has been given to conformal mapping for the purpose of calculating space differences. You will remember I mentioned that the very first numerical integrations done in meteorology employed finite Fourier transform techniques. There has been a revival of the idea of replacing space coordinates with wave number space for the entire system of equations. This is an extremely natural device for a sphere and one which evades many of the mapping difficulties. Some promising work has already been done (Platzman and Baer, 1959; Platzman, 1959) but it appears to be extremely taxing from a computational viewpoint. That is the matrix of coefficients consumes much more storage than do the dependent variables in the conventional finite difference formulation. Perhaps exploitation will have to await larger computing machines than are currently available.

F. Differences and Quadratures

There are a great variety of finite difference schemes that have been devised and employed. This is also true of quadrature formulae. The question often arises: for a given difference technique, is there a corresponding quadrature technique which is consistent in the sense that together they satisfy Stokes' theorem? We know we can devise consistent sets of this sort and the question is whether we should expect these sets to be unique. The problem of course is that there are certain physical integral constraints which are deducible from the continuous hydrodynamic equations such as the conservation of total westerly angular momentum for smooth boundaries. How does one know when one is conserving total angular momentum in finite differences? How does one measure it?

This brings us to a related question. Suppose there are a number of conservation principles deducible, e.g. that of total angular momentum and of total energy. However these principles apply to different powers of the velocity. Is it possible to devise a differencing scheme and a corresponding quadrature scheme which will simultaneously preserve both of the integral constraints irrespective of which continuous system is integrated numerically?

G. Elliptic Compatibility Conditions

As I have already indicated, in the early history of numerical applications in meteorology the severely constrained hydrodynamics gave rise to combined marching-jury problems. The result was that a great deal of effort was spent in learning to solve elliptic equations and the technique finally settled upon by most workers was relaxation by the extrapolated Liebmann technique. As attention turned to the Eulerian equations, the need for solving elliptic consistency conditions diminished. However, in preparing consistent initial conditions for the Eulerian equations, some sort of elliptic conditions will be necessary as a constraint—as was discussed earlier. Moreover, even in the Eulerian equations, if one wishes to eliminate external gravitational solutions but retain internal propagation, an elliptical condition must be satisfied which insures that the vertical integral of the divergence remain zero (Eliassen, 1956), i.e. that the last term of the inequality (1) vanish identically. Eliminating this constraint leaves a completely hyperbolic problem which requires reduced computational logic. The cost is that with the admission of higher frequency solutions the computation time is correspondingly longer due to shorter time steps.

The relative consequences are well demonstrated when one introduces condensation processes. In the quasi-geostrophic context there results a highly nonlinear two-dimensional Helmholtz equation (Smagorinsky, 1956) which is not only difficult to solve but in the final analysis stretches the geostrophic approximation beyond the point where it is valid. On the other hand, the introduction of condensation processes in the Eulerian equations gives rise to no special mathematical difficulty, and furthermore the hydrodynamic framework is physically more compatible with the process we are trying to describe.

H.   Computational Load

Most meteorological problems that have and probably will be dealt with by numerical methods depend very critically upon the inherent limitations of computing machines and of numerical techniques. I will take as an example a problem which represents an extreme—that is, the so-called study of the dynamics of the general circulation.

"The general circulation" is a somewhat ambiguous term in meteorology but for our purposes I will take it to denote the longer term, larger scale properties of the atmosphere, and the statistical dynamics of the transients of these properties. For example, what determines the distribution of easterly and westerly wind system in the lower part of the atmosphere and the general character of the westerlies in mid-atmosphere? What determines the space scale of disturbances in the westerlies and the time scale between maximum and minimum disturbance? How are these associated with the westerly angular momentum transport in the atmosphere, and why does a balance in the total westerly angular momentum tend to exist? What are the agencies primarily responsible for maintaining the heat balance in the atmosphere and what are the processes by which energy transformations are made between the ultimate radiative source and the ultimate dissipative sink? The answers to these questions will lead to an understanding of climatic changes and to practical dynamical methods of long range forecasting.

Short period evolutions of the order of one day are to a large extent inertial in the sense that they depend mainly upon the initial imbalance and to a much lesser extent upon the slowly acting energy sources and sinks. On the other hand, longer period changes are more in the nature of forced motions and hence depend less upon the details of the initial conditions and the inertial motions, although the statistical properties of the latter are important.

Let us therefore say that we wish to construct a model to study the dynamics of the general circulation which will cover the sphere with an average grid spacing of 200 km, therefore requiring 15,000 points in each pressure surface. In order to calculate radiative transfer as a function of the transmissive properties of the gaseous and particulate constituents of the atmosphere and also to calculate the turbulent transfer of heat, momentum and water vapor in the boundary layer would require approximately 10 mesh points in each vertical. Four dependent variables at each point: temperature, two horizontal wind components and water vapor content, must therefore require 6×10^5 pieces of data to describe the atmosphere at any one time. Assuming 16 multiplications per point in order to march one time step gives 10^7 multiplications per time step. For this horizontal grid interval, computational stability for the fastest moving admissible waves, in this case being the external gravitational waves, requires 5 minute time steps. A computing machine capable of 4000 multiplications per second would then compute at a rate 8 times <u>slower</u> than real time. This might not be serious if it were not necessary to perform experiments each with duration of a few months of real time.

I might point out that a much simpler general circulation model (Smagorinsky, 1959a), which has already yielded useful results in spite of its simplicity, computed at the rate of 16 times <u>faster</u> than real time on the 704. At the moment this is one of the most complex programs ever written in meteorology, requiring 10,000 instructions for the solution of the dynamic equations and for the output processing and analysis.

I have already indicated some of the sensitivities which can arise due to certain types of truncation error. However for long period integrations, even slow degeneracies may menace the outcome of the results.

I. Turbulence

In practice it is impossible to measure velocity components down to an arbitrarily small scale in the laboratory as well as in the atmosphere and it is necessary to establish a threshold of scale below which we no longer explicitly measure flow properties nor attempt to describe them dynamically——one may refer to this as the turbulence range. We then content ourselves with merely describing the statistical properties of the turbulence scale motions provided these statistics are stable in the sense that they can be deduced from the scale of motions that we are dealing with explicitly. Although the motions are not explicitly describable down to molecular scale, this is where the viscous dissipation occurs. So, we define a turbulence exchange coefficient which, taken with the strains in the fluid measured on the smallest explicit scale, determine the transformation of energy between the explicit motions and the turbulent motions. If we further postulate that the turbulent motions are steady in the sense that their energy does not change, then the energy transformation function must be identical to the rate of molecular viscous decay. In setting up a finite difference grid or a finite wave number space, a turbulent threshold is in effect defined and the question is how do the equations know to communicate with the molecular dissipation range? One of course finds empirically that, without any provision for dissipation, the cascade of kinetic energy to higher wave numbers ultimately increases the energy of the smallest wave resolvable by the grid. This energy has no place further to go, and ultimately the calculation departs from nature sufficiently to give intolerable truncation error. There have been some attempts to define a nonlinear viscosity such that the energy transformation function is consistent with similarity theory (Smagorinsky, 1959a). The undetermined parameter has the dimensions of a length squared, and empirically turns out to be some fraction of the grid size.

One cannot help get the feeling that perhaps turbulence itself could be studied digitally by experimenting with the threshold of turbulence. Of course, this is not a new idea—Batchelor alludes to it in his book (1953). I do not pretend to imply that the digital computer can replace the wind tunnel experimentally, but that each can provide insight not easily attainable from the other. In the atmosphere the apparent stresses in vertical planes are of a considerably more complex nature than the kind of turbulence which is normally studied. From approximately ten km down in horizontal scale, not only are the transformations of kinetic energy from low to high wave numbers, but there are also transformations of potential to kinetic energy due to buoyancy forces. This picture is further complicated by the fact that the release of latent heat changes the characteristics of the turbulence both in scale and intensity. The net effect is that there is not even an adequate parametric representation for the transport of momentum, heat and water vapor for this type of turbulence, which we call convection. We need to know what the classes of ambient states which are convectively unstable are, and then the statistical dynamics which describe the interaction between the turbulence and the mean motion, that is the systematic turbulent transport of heat, momentum and water vapor. Some work is now being done in an attempt to study these questions by digital simulation.

III. Concluding Remarks

Meteorology in contrast to most other physical sciences suffers from the fact that the atmosphere itself is virtually the only laboratory. The difficulty of course is obvious. One cannot perform controlled experiments in order to study isolated physical processes in their greatest simplicity. Instead, the entire gamut of influences are simultaneously operating as far as energy sources and dissipative sinks are concerned. Moreover, the kinematics of atmospheric flow are greatly complicated by the spectrum of disturbances excited by the earth's surface irregularities. To add to these difficulties, precise measurements with a density suitable for analysis are lacking. In retrospect it seems somewhat remarkable that so much has been gleaned from such inadequate observations of the atmosphere. In recent years some laboratory analogues have been constructed to simulate certain scales of motion in the atmosphere, and have proven extremely useful in providing an enhanced insight. Similarly the theoretical system of equations have lent themselves to limited analysis by linear techniques and more recently to higher order approximations. The virtues of this approach are obvious—one can examine the solutions as a continuous function of the parameters. As I have pointed out, filtering approximations have also proven extremely useful.

I would like to emphasize that computing machines cannot be considered a substitute for the ingenious mathematical and laboratory techniques of analysis which have been devised. Certainly the initial creative stages of any theoretical development must be done with pencil and paper. It is only when the simple readily accessible tests of validity are met, that the hypothesis is ready to stand or fall on the basis of the ultimate and conclusive tests of detailed numerical solution under arbitrary rather than idealized conditions. This is where the modern computing devices have their power: to carry a theoretical deduction to its logical conclusion. It is true that many of the processes which are essentially nonlinear in character are best studied by numerical means. However, experience shows that even in the case of these processes, considerable insight may be gained by the more conventional tools, and I might add the kind of insight that not often is reproducible by numerical experiment.

NOTES

*I have no intention of compiling an exhaustive list of credits, but rather to indicate turning points. Omissions must therefore not be construed as having lacked significance in the development of dynamic meteorology. An excellent bibliography is said to be found in a collection of papers edited by Saltzman (1958).

#Why the relative velocity is small is another matter having to do with the rate at which potential energy is produced by solar radiation.

§The need for such a moderating mechanism is noted in the fact that geostrophic models predict the formation of extra-tropical cyclones much too severely.

REFERENCES

Batchelor, G. K. , 1953, The Theory of Homogeneous Turbulence, Cambridge University Press, 197 pp.

Bjerknes, V. , 1901, Zirkulation relativ zu der Erde, Öfers. Vetenskaps-akad. Förh., Stockholm, 739-775.

Bjerknes, V. , 1904, Das Problem von der Wettervorhersage, betrachtet vom Standpunkt der Mechanik und der Physik, Meteor. Z., 21, 1-7.

Burger, A. , 1958, Scale considerations of planetary motions of the atmosphere, Tellus, 10, 195-205.

Charney, J. G. , 1947, The dynamics of long waves in a baroclinic westerly current, J. Meteor., 4, 135-162.

Charney, J. G. , 1948, On the scale of atmospheric motions, Geofys. Publikasjoner, Oslo, 17, No. 2, 17 pp.

Charney, J. G. , 1955, The use of the primitive equations of motion in numerical prediction, Tellus, 7, 22-26.

Charney, J. G. , and Eliassen, A. , 1949, A numerical method for predicting the perturbations of the middle latitude westerlies, Tellus, 1, 38-54.

Charney, J. G. , Fjørtoft, R. , and Neumann, J. v. , 1950, Numerical integration of the barotropic vorticity equation, Tellus, 2, 237-254.

Charney, J. G. , and Phillips, N. A. , 1953, Numerical integration of the quasi-geostrophic equations for barotropic and simple baroclinic flows, J. Meteor., 10, 71-99.

Eady, E. T. , 1949, Long waves and cyclone waves, Tellus, 1, 33-52.

Eliassen, A. , 1949, The quasi-static equations of motion with pressure as independent variable, Geofys. Publikasjoner, Oslo, 17, No. 3, 44 pp.

Eliassen, A. , 1956, A procedure for numerical integration of the primitive equations of the two-parameter model of the atmosphere, U. C. L. A. , Dept. of Meteor., Large Scale Synoptic Processes Project, Sc. Rep. 4, 53 pp.

Fjørtoft, R. , 1950, Application of integral theorems in deriving criteria of stability for laminar flows and for the baroclinic circular vortex, Geofys. Publikasjoner, Oslo, 17, No. 6, 52 pp.

Fjørtoft, R. , 1953, On the changes in the spectral distribution of kinetic energy for two-dimensional, nondivergent flow, Tellus, 5, 225-230.

Helmholtz, H. v., 1858, Über Integrale der hydrodynamischen Gleichungen welche den Wirbelbewegungen entsprechen, Jour.

reine u. angew. Math., 55, 25-55.

Helmholtz, H. v., 1888, Über atmosphärische Bewegungen, Meteor. Z., 5, 329-340.

Hinkelmann, K., 1959, Ein numerisches Experiment mit der primitiven Gleichungen, C.-G. Rossby Memorial Volume, Stockholm.

Høiland, E., 1941, On the stability of the circular vortex, Det Norske Videnskaps-Akademi i Oslo, Mat.-Naturv. Klasse, 11, 24 pp.

Jeffreys, H., 1926, On the dynamics of geostrophic winds, Quart J. Roy. Met. Soc., 52, 85-104.

Knox, J. B., 1958, The time integration of the barotropic model, unpublished.

Kuo, H.-L., 1949, Dynamic instability of two-dimensional non-divergent flow in a barotropic atmosphere, J. Meteor., 6, 105-122.

Lin, C. C., 1945, On the stability of two-dimensional parallel flow, Q. Appl. Math., 3, 117-142, 218-234, 277-301.

Margules, M., 1903, Uber die Energie der Sturme, Jahrb. Zentral-Anst. Meteor. Geodynamik, 40, Vienna.

Phillips, N. A., 1951, A simple three-dimensional model for the study of large-scale extratropical flow patterns, J. Meteor., 8, 381-394.

Phillips, N.A., 1957a, A coordinate system having some special advantages for numerical forecasting, J. Meteor., 14, 184-185.

Phillips, N.A., 1957b, A map projection system suitable for large-scale numerical weather prediction, J. Meteor. Soc. Japan, 75th Anniv. Vol., 262-267.

Phillips, N. A., 1959a, Numerical integration of the primitive equations on a hemisphere, Monthly Weather Review, 87.

Phillips, N. A., 1959b, On the problem of initial data for the primitive equations, M.I.T., Dept. of Meteorology.

Platzman, G.W., 1958, The lattice structure of the finite difference primitive and vorticity equations, Monthly Weather Review, 86, 285-292.

Platzman, G.W., 1959, The spectral form of the vorticity equation, U. of Chicago, Dept. of Meteorology, 51 pp.

Platzman, G. W., and Baer, F., 1959, Numerical integration of the spectral vorticity equation, U. of Chicago, Dept. of Meteor.

Rayleigh, Lord, 1913, On the stability of the laminar motion of an inviscid fluid, Phil. Mag., 26, 1001-1010.

Richardson, L. F. , 1922, Weather prediction by numerical process, Cambridge University Press, 236 pp.

Rossby, C. -G. , and Collaborators, 1939, Relation between variations in the intensity of the zonal circulation of the atmosphere and the displacement of the semi-permanent centers of action, J. Marine Res., 2, 38-55.

Rossby, C. -G. , 1940, Planetary flow patterns in the atmosphere, Quart. J. Roy. Met. Soc., 66 (supplement), 68-87.

Saltzman, B. (Editor), 1958, The general circulation as a problem in thermal convection—a collection of classical and modern theoretical papers, M. I. T. , Department of Meteorology, General Circulation Project, Scientific Report No. 1, 416 pp.

Smagorinsky, J. , 1956, On the inclusion of moist adiabatic processes in numerical prediction models, Symposium über Numerishe Wettervorhersage in Frankfurt a. M. , Bericht des Deutschen Wetterdienstes, 38, 82-90.

Smagorinsky, J. , 1958, On the numerical integration of the primitive equations of motion for baroclinic flow in a closed region, Monthly Weather Review, 86, 457-466.

Smagorinsky, J. , 1959a, General circulation experiments with the primitive equations, to be published.

Smagorinsky, J. , 1959b, to be published.

Solberg, H. , 1936, Le mouvement d'inertie de l'atmosphère stable et son rôle dans la théorie des cyclones, Un. Geod. Geophys. Int., VI Assembly, Edinburgh, 66-82.

Discussion of Paper Eight

Dr. Lanczos: As far as the observation of meteorological data goes, it occurs to me that if the observations were made in an exactly rectangular grid, one could use an entirely different kind of numerical technique. I inquired about that, and they told me that for practical reasons it was rather difficult to do so. In my opinion the use of the Fourier series for interpolation (and possibly) extrapolation purposes could have great advantages.

Dr. Smagorinsky: I think the greatest advantage would be to insure uniform data density over the surface of the earth. The fact that it would be in a rectangular array I think is not too relevant—it being more a question of esthetics than of necessity. The checkerboard array is of course what Richardson had in mind.

Index

A

Aberdeen, 18
Adams, 46
aerodynamic incidence, 68
    noise, 64
aeroelasticity, 59 passim
adjoint system, 105
aileron buzz, 63
albedo factor, 27
Alder, 90
allocation of resources, 70
    of effort, 71
Amaldi, 28
approximation, few-group, 27
    geostrophic, 110
    quasi-nondivergent, 110
atmosphere, properties of large
    scale motions, 107
    quasi-baratropic character,
    108
atmospheric, density, 49
    drags, relative magnitude of,
    58
    neutral drag, 56
atmospheric resistance, 47, 48,
    49, 50
    radial decelerations from, 47,
    48
axisymmetric fluid motions, 100

B

Baer, 116
Bareiss, 36
baroclinic instability, 109
barotropic, non-linear forecasts,
    110
Batchelor, 119
Bauschinger effect, 3
Bellman, 26

Bessel, 45
Biot, 61
Bjerknes, V., 107
Boltzman equation, 88
Born-Oppenheimer separation,
    93, 94
boundaries, extrapolated, 27
boundary layer mechanisms, 65
Brown, E. W., 46, 51
Brownian motions, 17
Bullen, 57
Burger, 114

C

Carlson's S_n method, 35
cell calculations, 27
Chapman-Enskog, 89, 90
characteristic value problems,
    non-linear, linear functions
    of, 102
Charney, 109
Chebyshev polynomial tech-
    niques, 35
chemical reaction rates, 91
    calculation of, 92, 94
    collisional basis, 91
chemistry, theoretical,
    83 passim
chemistry, theoretical develop-
    ments, empirical theories, 83
    application of theoretical
    physics, 83
circulation theorem, 107
Clairaut's equation, 46, 57
compatibility conditions,
    elliptic, 116
computers, high-speed, 85
    digital, 72

computers (continued)
    ENIAC, 109
    IBM 704, 73, 90
    ILLIAC, 94
condensation processes, 117
Conte, 106
control reversal, 59
convection, 119
Coolidge, 85, 86
Coriolis parameter, 108
Couette flow, inviscid, 102
Coulson, 86
cross-sections, microscopic, 24
    macroscopic, 24
Curtiss, 89
cyclones, extratropical, 108, 120

D

Dahler, 90
d'Alembert, 46
Davis, 36
degrees of freedom, electronic,
    nuclear, 93
Delaunay, 46
detonations, 91
differential principle of Greenberg,
    7
Dirac, 83
distribution functions, 88
Doppler broadening, 38
Douglas, 35
drag, neutral, 58
    electromagnetic, 58
    atmospheric neutral, 58

E

Eady, 109
Earnshaw piston theory, 64
earth,
    as a perfect fluid. 56
    center of gravity, 56
    internal structure, 57
    mapping of surface, 115
    material currents in core, 56
    motions in core, 56
Eckert, Wallace, 99
Edie, Leslie E., 75
Ehrenfest, 94
eigenvalue problems for ordinary

differential equation systems,
    numerical techniques on high-
    speed computers, 105
Eisenhart, 85
elastic strain energy, 5
electromagnetic drag, 58
electromagnetic viscosity, see
    induction drag
Eliassen, 109, 111, 113, 114,
    117
elongation, plastic, 3
    elastic, 3
energies, binding, 85, 87
Enskog, see Chapman-Enskog
equations,
    multi-group diffusion, 26,
        27, 31
    one-region reactor kinetic, 26
equilibrium, gravitational of an
    incompressible fluid mass
    with axisymmetric fluid mo-
    tions and magnetic fields,
    100.
ergodic, quasi-, hypothesis, 90
Euler, 45, 46
Eulerian equations, 107-112
    applicability of Eulerian
    equations to the atmosphere,
    107
    quasi-static, 111
    numerical integration, 111
Evard, 62
Eyring, 94

F

FE-MO (free-electron molecular-
    orbital), 86
Fermi age theory, 28
finite difference schemes, 116
fission product poisoning, 38
Fjørtoft, 109, 110
flutter, 59, 60
fourth-harmonic, 56
    distortion, terrestrial, 56
Frobenius, 31
    -Perron theory, 32
fuel depletion calculations, 38

G

Garabedian, 65
Gauss, 45
Gelbard, 36
Grad, 89
gravitational noise, 48, 58
Greenberger, Martin, 76

H

Habetler, 32
Hansen, 46
Hayes, Wally, 63
Helmholtz equation, 33, 35,
    107, 108, 111
Henry, A. F., 37
Hilbert, 89
Hill, 46
Hinkelmann, 111, 113
Høiland, 111
hydroelasticity, 67
hydromagnetics, 99

I

IAD method (implicit alternating
    direction), 35, 43
induction drag, 47, 50
integral equation, Kirkwood, 90
integral principle of Haar and
    von Mises, 7
integral, vis-viva, 52
inventory management, 70, 74
ionosphere, 50
iterations, inner, 33
    outer, 33, 34

J

Jacchia, L. E., 49
Jacobi, 51
James, 85, 86
Jeffreys, 108
Jentzsch, theorem of, 31
Jones, W. P., 64

K

Kalaba, 26
kernel, migration, 24, 33, 29
kinetic theory, generalization
    of, 89

Kirkwood, 89
    (see also integral equation,
    Kirkwood)
Knox, 113
Korbel, 76
Kozyrev, 56
Kuo, 109
Kuster, 60
Kutta condition, 62

L

Lagrange, 45, 52
Laplace, 45, 46
Lees, 65
lethargy groups, 33
Leverrier, 45
Levinson, N., 97
Lieberstein, 65
Liebmann technique, 116
Liebowitz, Martin, 28
Lighthill, 63, 65
Lin, C. C., 65, 109
Liouville equation, 88
Luniks (Russian), 51

M

magnetohydrodynamics, 99
    passim
Margules, 107
Markov process, 72
    generalized, 30
    matrices, 72
Marshak, 27
Martin, M. H., 97
Martino, 32
mass ratio, 67
matrices, density 87
    nonnegative, theory of, 30
    p-cyclic, 34
Maxwell's equation, 50
Mercury's perihelion, 45
meteorology,
    computational load, 117
    dynamic, evolution of, 107
    equations arising in, 107
    initial data, 112
    lateral boundary conditions,
    113

meteorology (continued)
    time integration, 113
    vertical boundary conditions,
      114
    vertical truncation error, 114
Milne's equation, on computing
    machines, 44
Minitrack stations, 47
MO-LCAO (molecular-orbital
    linear-combination-of-atomic-
    orbitals), 86
molecular beams, 90
molecules,
    diatomic, 85
    triatomic, 85
    energy of interaction between,
      86
    non-spherical, 89
    rigid sphere, 90
Monge-Ampére equation, 110
Monte Carlo method, 24, 36, 73,
    77, 79, 82, 90
moon, 45 passim
    eccentricity of orbit, 51
    lunar motion, analytic theories
      of, 46
Moulton, F.R., 52
Muller, David, 106
multiplication factor, 24
multiplicative processes, 29

N

Navier-Stokes, 65
neutral drag, 58
neutrons, 24 passim
    average yield, 24
    delayed, 25, 37
    fast, 27
    fission, 23
    flux, 26
    life cycle, 23
    monoenergetic, 26
    paths, 29
    slow, 27
    thermal, 23, 26, 38
Newton, 45, 46
    laws of particle dynamics, 107
numerical analysis role in dynamic
    aspects of plasticity, 17

O

operation, definition, 69
operations research, 79
Oppenheimer, see Born-
    Oppenheimer
Orcutt, Guy, 76
Orr-Sommerfeld, 65
overrelaxation, 34
    line, 34
    block, 34
ozone, 87

P

parameter, buckling, 28
Peaceman, 35
Pearson, 36
Pekeris, 85
Perron, 30
    -Frobenius theory, 32, 36
persistent distribution; impor-
    tance vector, 30
perturbation methods, 87
perturbations,
    due to attraction of the sun
      and moon, 51
    from rotational distortion of
      earth, 47
    lunar, 55
    solar, 55
Phillips, 110, 111, 113, 114,
    115
Pioneers (American), 51
plasma, partially ionized, of the
    upper air, 91
plastic flow, alternating, pro-
    gressive, 8
plastic limit analysis in the
    continuum, 20
plastic range, 3
plasticity, numerical analysis
    role in dynamic aspects of,
    17
Platzman, 113, 116
Poincare, 45, 51
Poisson distribution, 74
polynomial techniques, Cheby-
    shev, 35
Possio, 60, 61

pressure, normalized by the surface pressure, 114
Prigogine, 89
programming,
differential quadratic, 17
linear, 71
quadratic, 7
quadratic differential, 11
quadrature formulae, 116
quantum mechanics, 86, 87
quasi-geostrophic elliptic consistency condition, 111

R

Rachford, 35
radiative transfer, theory, 26
Rayleigh, 109
-Ritz variational principle, 85
reactors, 23 passim
critical, 25, 24, 31
dynamics, 37
idealized homogeneous, 23
kinetics, 37, 38
mathematical models, 25
statics, main problem of, 32
thermal, 23
reactor stability, short-term, 38
Redheffer, M., 97
Reissner, 61
resonance absorption, 24
restricted problem of three
bodies, 51
Richardson, 107, 108
Rossby, 108, 109
Routh's laws of dynamics, 59

S

Saltzman, 120
satellite, artificial, 45 passim
apogee distances, 48
perigee distances, 48
revolution , average period
of, 49
Schrödinger equation, 84, 87, 93
approximate solution for
molecules, 85
coordinate systems, 85
search,
basic problem, 71

search (continued)
band, 71
general problems, 71
second-harmonic rotational
distortion, 48, 51
semi-diurnal tides, terrestrial,
48
lunar, 48
solar, 48
separability, concept of, 83
separation of variables, generalizations of the methods of,
97
shake-down, 20
SHARE, 7
shock tubes, 91
Solberg, 111
solid, perfectly plastic, 3
work-hardening, 3
Sommerfeld, see Orr-Sommerfeld
Sommerfeld radiation condition, 62
SOR method (systematic overrelaxation) 34, 44
spacing noise, 76
Spanier, J., 36
spectral theory, 28
Sputnik III, 49
irregularities of motion, 50
statically admissible stress
field, 20
stochastic forces,
external, 72
internal, 72
Stokes, see Navier-Stokes
stress, residual state of, 7
stress analysis, 3
stress field, statically admissible, 20

T

Taylor, 92
temperature, local, 91
temperature coefficients, reactivity, 38
Theodorsen, 60
theory, game, 70, 71
search, 70
third harmonic, 56, 57, 58
Thomas, L. H., 99

tidal distortion, 58
torsional divergence, 59
trajectories, periodic, 52
transport calculations, 35
    theory, 25
truncation error, 34
truss, approximating a continuous
    part by, 19
    with friction at the joints of
        the bars, 19
    perfectly plastic, 5
turbines, steam, flutter in, 67
turbulence, 118

V

Vanguard I, 49
    irregularities of motion, 50
Varga, R. S., 31
variational formulation of non-
    self-adjoint characteristic
    value problems in high order
    differential equations, 101
variational principles, 87
velocity-groups, 27
viscosity, nonlinear, 119
von Neumann, 109

W

Wall, 94
Whipple, F. L., 48
Wilkins, 27
Wood, 90

Y

yield
    polygon, 6, 10
    forces, 3
Young, 35